SCRIBNER READING SERIES

LOOK AROUND YOU

Jack Cassidy

Doris Roettger   *Karen K. Wixson*

SCRIBNER EDUCATIONAL PUBLISHERS
New York

ACKNOWLEDGMENTS
Portions of this text have been adapted from materials originally prepared under the direction of Dr. Charles Walcutt and Dr. Glenn McCracken.

"The Goat in the Rug" from THE GOAT IN THE RUG by Charles L. Blood and Martin Link. Text Copyright © 1976 by Charles L. Blood and Martin Link. Adapted with permission of Four Winds Press, an imprint of Macmillan Publishing Company.

"In Case of Fire" by Nona Keen Duffy is from JACK AND JILL magazine. Copyright © 1985 by Benjamin Franklin Literary & Medical Society, Inc., Indianapolis, Indiana. Reprinted by permission of the publisher.

"Leo, Zack and Emmie" adapted from LEO, ZACK AND EMMIE by Amy Ehrlich. Copyright © 1981 by Amy Ehrlich. Reprinted by permission of the publisher, Dial Books for Young Readers and the author.

"The Library" by Barbara A. Huff originally appeared in FAVORITE POEMS OLD AND NEW edited by Helen Ferris, Doubleday 1957. "The Library" is Copyright © 1957 by Barbara A. Huff and is reprinted with her permission.

"Midge and Fred" is the adaptation of the entire text of MIDGE AND FRED by Brian Schatell (J. B. Lippincott). Copyright © 1983 by Brian Schatell. By permission of Harper & Row, Publishers, Inc.

"The Monstrous Glisson Glop" from THE MONSTROUS GLISSON GLOP by Diane Redfield Massie. Copyright © 1970 by Diane Redfield Massie. Reprinted by permission of the author.

"Morris Has A Cold" is an adaptation of the text of MORRIS HAS A COLD by Bernard Wiseman. Copyright © 1978 by Bernard Wiseman. Reprinted by permission of Dodd, Mead & Company, Inc.
(continued on page 256)

SCRIBNER EDUCATIONAL PUBLISHERS
866 Third Avenue
New York, NY 10022
Collier Macmillan Publishers, London
Collier Macmillan Canada, Inc.

Printed in the United States of America
ISBN 0-02-256080-7
9 8 7 6 5 4 3 2 1

LOOK
AROUND YOU

Contents

PROMISES AND SURPRISES 1

MIDGE and FRED

by Brian Schatell

One day Midge Biffle met a man named Mr. Blueberry. Read the story to find out what Mr. Blueberry did. Why did Midge want to teach him a lesson?

Part 1: Midge's Best Friend

Midge Biffle and her pet fish, Fred, were the best of friends.

Every day they played together, and ate together, and watched TV together.

But their favorite thing to do together was to balance things on Fred's nose. With Midge cheering him on, Fred could balance anything.

One day, a strange car drove onto Midge's block, pulling behind it a large, boxy shape on wheels.

The driver got out, and with one
sharp jerk pulled the cover off the box.
Underneath, was a gigantic glass fish
tank. Inside the tank were strange and
colorful fish.

In a little while, some people came
down the street.

"Ah, customers!" the man snickered
to himself. But the people went on past,
with barely a glance.

The man tried everything, but
nothing worked. "Hey, what's going on
here?" he growled, and he ran after
them.

There was Fred, balancing a bottle
of milk, a cactus, a tea kettle, a hammer,
and a bowl of spaghetti and meat balls.

"Wow," the man yelled. "What a talented fish! With a fish like that, my aquarium could make millions!"

When the crowd left, the man grabbed a ladder from his car and went up to Midge's window ledge.

"Hey! What are *you* doing up here?" Midge cried.

"Let me introduce myself," said the man as he handed her a fancy card. "I'm Mr. Blueberry, owner of Blueberry's Traveling Aquarium. I need a fish like that for my show."

Fred and Midge looked at each other in horror. "Oh, No!" said Midge. "Fred is my best friend!" and Fred nodded in agreement.

"Oh, well," said Mr. Blueberry. "I just felt that I could teach Fred some *real* tricks."

"Oh?" asked Midge. "What sort of tricks?"

14

"Well, I've traveled all over the world. To me a balancing fish isn't a balancing fish unless . . . er . . . uh—" and Mr. Blueberry spied a fruit peddler down below—"unless it can balance a watermelon on its nose!"

"Wow!" said Midge. "I've never seen Fred balance a watermelon before!"

"Well, then," replied Mr. Blueberry, "I *can* help! Why don't you look for a watermelon now!"

While she was looking, Mr. Blueberry snatched Fred's fishbowl.

Part 2: Midge Saves Fred

"I've been tricked!" screamed
Midge. "Fred's been fishnapped!" She
went down the ladder, but it was too
late. Mr. Blueberry and his aquarium
were speeding away.

"I'll save Fred from that fishnapper
if it's the last thing I do!" cried Midge.

"And I'll help you!" said the fruit
peddler angrily. "That fishnapper tipped
over my cart!"

Just then, they noticed a trail of water in the street, and at once they followed it. Before long, they came to a big crowd of people.

"My fish is the greatest balancing fish in the seven seas!" Mr. Blueberry was telling the crowd.

But the crowd was grumbling, "We've seen a fish balance *those* things before."

"Hey! That's *my* fish!" cried Midge angrily, and she worked her way to the front of the crowd.

Midge yelled, "I was told that a balancing fish isn't a balancing fish unless it can balance a watermelon!"

"Hey!" yelled a man next to her. "That's a real trick. Let's see him balance a watermelon!"

"Yes!" said a woman in back of her. "Let's see Blueberry's fish balance *two* watermelons!"

"Or *three* watermelons!" said another. "Can't he do it, Blueberry?" asked someone else.

"Uh . . ." Mr. Blueberry said, "we can't do that trick today. I don't have any watermelons."

"Oh, yes you do," said the fruit peddler, wheeling his cart up. "You have ten of them!"

"Oh, No!" groaned Mr. Blueberry, and thud, thud, thud, thud, thud, thud, thud, thud, thud, thud, the peddler dumped them at his feet.

Splash, splash, splash, splash, splash, splash. Fred let everything he had on his nose drop into the water.

18

The crowd grew silent as Mr. Blueberry lifted the first melon. Leaning shakily over the edge of the big tank, he placed it on Fred's nose.

A gasp rose from the crowd—and the watermelon balanced!

Then Mr. Blueberry lifted a second melon, and then a third, and Fred balanced those, too!

Mr. Blueberry became more and more confident. By the time all ten melons were balanced, the crowd was wide-eyed. Mr. Blueberry smiled. "*My fish can balance anything!*"

But he couldn't. SHMUSCH!!! All ten watermelons came tumbling down, and SMLOSH, fell and broke all over Mr. Blueberry. SMLOSH, SMLOSH, SMLOSH, SMLOSH!!! He was a mess!

"My show is done for!" wailed Mr. Blueberry.

But the crowd cheered and clapped and stomped their feet. "That was the best part of the show!" they roared. "More! We want more!!"

"Oh, NO!" moaned Mr. Blueberry. "This is terrible." And Fred winked at Midge.

"Give me back my fish!" commanded Midge.

"Take him, take him, PLEASE take him!" said Mr. Blueberry.

Midge was so happy that she jumped up and down and kissed Fred.

Mr. Blueberry complained, "But now no one will want to see my show. My fish can't do anything."

"If you promise never to fishnap again," replied Midge, "then Fred will teach *your* fish to balance."

"I promise! I promise!" said Mr. Blueberry.

So Fred gave them lessons, and Mr. Blueberry's Traveling Aquarium became the biggest hit in town!

CHECK FOR UNDERSTANDING

1. What did Mr. Blueberry say a balancing fish had to do?
2. How did the crowd trick him?
3. Will Mr. Blueberry keep the promise he gave Midge? Why or why not?

silent b

| comb | lamb | thumb | debt |
| climb | limb | crumb | doubt |

silent l

| talk | could | half | calm |
| walk | would | calf | palm |

Fire-Safety Tips

Fire can be very useful. But it also can be very dangerous. Fires can happen anywhere—at home, at school, or at work.

Each year in the United States, thousands of people are burned or killed in fires. Forests, homes, and stores are burned to the ground. Valuable property is lost by fire.

Fires can start in many ways. Many fires are started by children playing with matches. Fires are often started by people falling asleep while smoking. Fires can start if you are careless with candles or portable heaters. Many fires start in the kitchen when someone forgets something that is cooking on the stove.

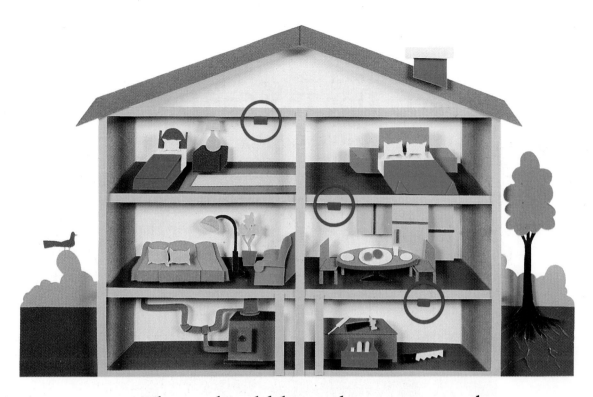

There should be at least one smoke detector on every floor or level of a home. A smoke detector makes a loud buzzing sound when smoke reaches it. This sound warns you that a fire could be starting somewhere in the house.

Many fires start when people are sleeping. The smoke detector can wake you up and give you more time to get out safely. A smoke detector should be checked once a month to see if it is working properly.

Safety Tips That Can Help Save Lives

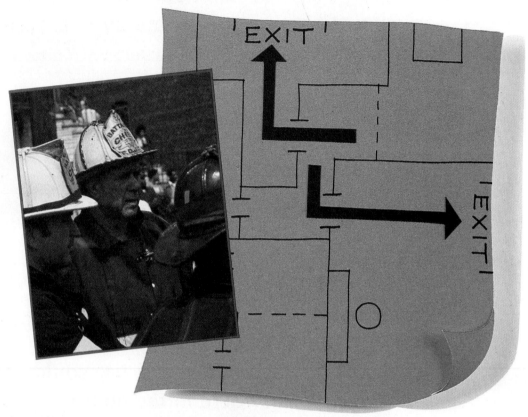

1. **Plan a Home Fire Drill.**

    Talk with your family and decide on the safest and fastest way to get out of your house or apartment. Then, practice your home fire drill as if a fire had really started.

If you live in a house, you should have at least two ways to get out—the front and back doors. If you live in an apartment, locate the fire escape. Decide how to get out of rooms on the top floors. You can use the stairs to exit. Never use the elevator. It may become trapped between floors.

You may need to use a rope or ladder to escape. Keep them near a window. Be sure you know how to open locked windows and how to go down a ladder, if necessary.

2. Sleep With Bedroom Doors Closed.

This should help to keep out heat and smoke if a fire starts while you are sleeping. However, make sure that you can hear the smoke detector when your bedroom door is closed.

3. Stay Calm.

Fire is scary, but try not to panic. Shout, "FIRE!" Pound on doors and walls. Wake up and warn others.

4. Feel any Door Before you Open it.

If the door feels hot, DO NOT OPEN IT! If the door feels cool, open it just a crack. Close the door quickly if heat or smoke rushes in. Keep the smoke out by sealing any cracks around the door with sheets, towels, or clothing.

5. Go to a Window.

Smoke may prevent your exit from the door. Use the window as a second way to escape a fire. Open a window. Then shout for help. Wave a sheet or a towel to signal for help. Do not climb out the window. Wait by the window until help comes.

6. Stay Close to the Floor.

Remember that heat and smoke rise. You can breathe best if you stay close to the floor where the air is cooler and less smoky. It will help if you can place a wet cloth or towel over your nose and mouth. Crawl on your hands and knees to the nearest exit.

7. If Your Clothes Catch on Fire, Don't Run. Stop. Drop. Roll.

Drop and roll on the floor or the ground to smother the fire. Grab a blanket, a small rug, or a coat. Wrap it around you to put out the flames.

8. **Know how to Report a Fire to Your Fire Department.**

Once you get outside, go directly to a meeting place which you and your family have decided on. Know the location of the nearest telephone or fire alarm box. Call the fire department and give them your name, full street address, and town. Remain there until help arrives.

Be Alert. Help Prevent Fires. Plan And Practice Now!

CHECK FOR UNDERSTANDING

1. Name two ways fires can start.
2. Why is a smoke detector important?
3. Which three words should you remember if your clothes catch on fire?

IN CASE OF FIRE

by Nona Keen Duffy

In case of fire in your home
Things depend on you.
You may save a life sometime
By knowing what to do!

Know what fire signals are.
Hurry, but don't run.
Report the fire if you can,
Or notify someone.

32

Don't get scared and lose your head;
Think fast by keeping cool.
Obey the teacher if a fire
Should happen at your school.

If your clothes should catch on fire,
Don't yell and run about,
Just quickly roll upon a rug
And put the fire out!

There may be a fire sometime
When you are all alone.
You may save a person's life,
And it may be your own!

33

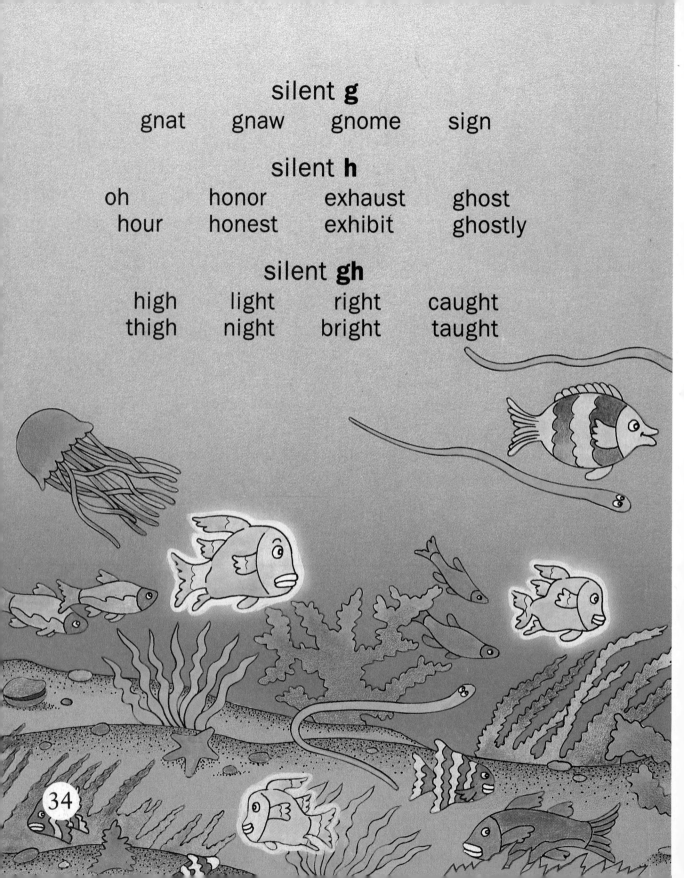

silent **g**

gnat	gnaw	gnome	sign

silent **h**

oh	honor	exhaust	ghost
hour	honest	exhibit	ghostly

silent **gh**

high	light	right	caught
thigh	night	bright	taught

Monstrous Glisson Glop

by Diane Redfield Massie

There was a monstrous Glisson Glop
Who lived beneath the sea.
His eyes were red. His teeth were sharp
And greener than a pea.

"I love to dine on lantern fish,
And eels are better yet.
The more I eat," the monster said,
"The darker, still, it gets!"

"It's gloomy on the ocean floor.
It's blacker than the night.
And if I eat the lantern fish,
There won't be any light."

He ate another lantern fish.
And swallowed down an eel.
"A pity!" said the Glisson Glop.
"How sad it makes me feel."

He found his tattered storybook
And held it to his face.
"I can't make out the words," he said.
"I'll never find my place!"

"I mustn't eat another eel!"
An eel came swimming by.
He gulped it up and licked his chops.
"It makes me want to cry!"

"The sea is black as ink," he said.
"It's hard to see my claws.
If lantern fish come swimming by,
I'm buttoning my jaws."

The lantern fish came swimming past.
He ate them one by one.
"I've finished off the lantern fish,
And now," he sighed, "there's none."

"What *will* I do?" He wrung his claws.
"A Glisson Glop needs light!
I'm frightened of the dark!" he said.
"Somehow this isn't right!"

He lay upon the ocean floor.
"It's day . . . or is it night?
One can't," he said, "tell what it is.
I wish I had a light."

"I wish I had a lantern fish
And one electric eel.
I'd never think again," he said,
"Of making them a meal."

"I'd treat them very gently.
I'd pat them on the head.
I'd read them bedtime stories, too,
Before they went to bed."

The Glisson Glop sat sadly down
And strained his eyes to see.
"The black is even blacker
Than it ever used to be."

"What's that?" he said. "Some little
        lights!
THEY'RE COMING NEAR! HOORAY!
A lantern fish and eel," he said,
"Are surely on their way!"

A little fish came swimming by
With lights above his head.
The Glisson Glop fell on his knees.
"A LIGHT!" the monster said.

"Stay here!" he told the little fish.
"Come near so I can see!"
"Why should I?" said the little fish.
"Perhaps you might eat *me*."

41

"Perhaps I won't," the Glisson Glop
Said crossly from his bed.
"I hate the dark. It strains my eyes
And makes them very red."

"My promises," the Glisson Glop
Said, "probably are good.
I try my best to keep them.
When I don't, I know I should."

"I'm going!" said the little fish.
He quickly swam away.
"Outrageous!" said the Glisson Glop.
"What *can* a monster say?"

A lantern fish swam slowly by
A blue electric eel.
"I PROMISE NOT TO EAT YOU!
OH, HOW WONDERFUL I FEEL!"

The lantern fish and eel swam down.
They climbed upon his knee.
And now the monster reads at night.
"It's hard," he says, "when one can't bite
Or nibble up one's reading light.
But *oh*! It's nice to see."

STEPS TO FOLLOW

WHEN YOU FIRST MEET A NEW WORD

SAY THE WORD.
Is it a word that you have heard before?

LOOK AT THE WORD.
Can you break the word into parts? Do you know the meanings of the parts?

READ THE SENTENCE IN WHICH THE WORD APPEARS.
Do the other words in the sentence help you understand the new word?

If you are still not sure what the word means, look it up in a dictionary.

STEPS TO FOLLOW
WHEN YOU WRITE

PREWRITING—Before you write,
- choose a topic, something you want to write about.
- think about who will read what you write.
- make notes on what you want to write about.

WRITING—When you write,
- use your notes to put your ideas together.
- write a topic sentence that tells the main idea.
- write some sentences that tell more about the main idea.

REVISING—After you write,
- read what you wrote.
- edit it. Make sure it makes sense and says what you want it to say.
- proofread it. Make sure your spelling and punctuation marks are correct.

Use these marks when you edit and proofread		
	⁋	Start new paragraph
	∧	Add this
	✎	Take this out
	⁄lowercase	Make this lowercase
	capital	Make this uppercase

- copy your work on a clean sheet of paper.

short **e** spelled **ea**

head	ready	bread	breath
read	heavy	thread	breakfast
dead	healthy	spread	weather
deaf	wealthy	instead	feather

long **a** spelled **ea**

| great | break | steak | daybreak |

Clouds Tell About the Weather

Long ago, people did not have TV sets, radios, or newspapers to tell them what the weather would be like. They looked at the clouds for signs of coming weather. They discovered that when the clouds changed, the weather changed, too.

What do you see in these clouds? Do you see great big feathers? Do you see curls of hair?

Clouds form in different shapes and sizes. Each kind of cloud has a name. These are called *cirrus* clouds. *Cirrus* is the Latin word for *hair*. Cirrus clouds are thin and look very light and fluffy. They float across the top of the sky, holding only a little water. Cirrus clouds mean pleasant weather.

What do you see when you look at these clouds?

These are called *cumulus* clouds. *Cumulus* is a Latin word that means *heap*. Some people think cumulus clouds look like heaps of whipped cream. Other people think they look like fat sheep or giant puffs of cotton.

Cumulus clouds can get big and heavy. The weather is changing. There is a good chance there will be showers.

But, if you look carefully, you can see that the thinner edges of these clouds are much brighter. Even the darkest clouds have a silvery border.

This is the sun coming through. People say, "Every cloud has a silver lining," when they want to cheer someone up.

Sometimes the cumulus clouds become storm clouds. They are called *thunderheads* and can bring dreadful weather—thunder, lightning, hail, and high winds.

These are called *stratus* clouds. *Stratus* comes from a Latin word that means *spread out*. These clouds spread out across the sky like a thin white sheet. Stratus clouds mean good weather.

But, sometimes stratus clouds come close to the ground. This is what causes fog. Sometimes it is hard to see through the fog. Drivers may not be able to see us. In foggy weather, we must be very careful and watch for cars when we cross the street.

Who can help us know more about the weather? People called *meteorologists* can help us. They have many tools to help them tell us what the weather will be like.

They use balloons that carry devices called *radiosondes*. The balloons go up in the air twice a day and send back signals by radio. These signals tell what is going on high above us.

Meteorologists also get information from weather *satellites* in space that take pictures of the clouds. These pictures show the cloud patterns and how the clouds are moving all over our planet.

Weather conditions are also reported from every airport across the world. This information helps meteorologists see patterns in weather. They also use *radar*. Radar helps them find where it is raining and which way the rain is going. Is it heading our way?

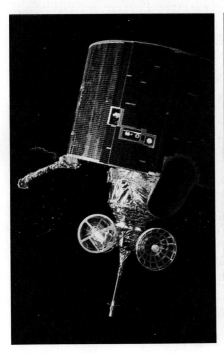

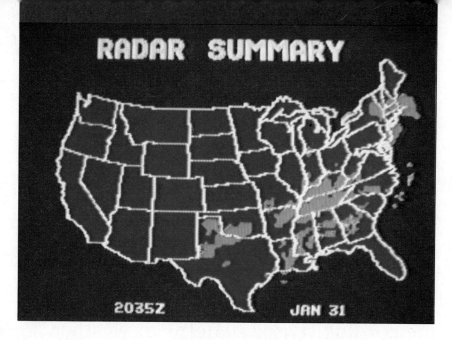

RADAR SUMMARY

2035Z   JAN 31

All of this information is used to help make weather maps. Then, meteorologists at weather stations can use these maps to write weather reports. Most of the time, the weather reports on radio and TV are right. But sometimes the weather surprises everyone.

No one can ever really be sure when the clouds will change. The only thing we can be sure of is that nothing changes more than the weather.

CHECK FOR UNDERSTANDING
1. How do clouds tell about the weather?
2. What kind of information do meteorologists get from satellites?

ear in **earth**

earth	learn	heard	pearl
earn	learned	search	early

ear in **bear**

bear	pear	wear	tear

ear in **heart**

heart	hearth

55

THE COW

by Robert Louis Stevenson

The friendly cow, all red and white,
　　I love with all my heart:
She gives me cream with all her might,
　　To eat with apple-tart.

She wanders lowing here and there,
　　And yet she cannot stray,
All in the pleasant open air,
　　The pleasant light of day;

And blown by all the winds that pass
　　And wet with all the showers,
She walks among the meadow grass
　　And eats the meadow flowers.

56

Morris Has a Cold

by Bernard Wiseman

Even easy words can be hard to understand. Read this story to see how Boris and Morris have a hard time with easy words.

Morris the Moose said, "I have a cold. My nose is walking."

Boris the Bear said, "You mean your nose is running."

"No," said Morris. "My nose is walking. I only have a little cold."

Boris said, "Let me feel your forehead."

Morris said, "I don't have four heads!"

Boris said, "I know you don't have four heads. But this is called your forehead."

Morris said, "That is my ONE head."

"All right," Boris the Bear growled. "Let me feel your one head."

Boris said, "Your one head feels hot. That means you are sick. You need some rest. You should lie down."

Morris lay down.

"Not HERE!" Boris shouted. "You are sick. You must lie down on a bed."

Morris asked, "What is a bed?"

"Well," said Boris, "a bed has four legs. . . . "

"Ohhh," Morris said, "I will not lie down on a bed! I might get hurt."

Boris asked, "How can you get hurt if you lie down on a bed?"

"A bed has legs," said Morris. "I might fall off the bed when it jumps or runs."

Boris said, "Beds do not jump. Beds do not run. Beds just stand still."

"Why?" asked Morris. "Are beds lazy?"

"No!" Boris shouted. "Beds are not lazy! Beds are . . . Oh, come with me—I will show you a bed."

"Here we are," said Boris. "This is the Town Dump. People leave things here. We should find a bed here. Help me look for one. Look for a thing with four legs."

Morris yelled, "This has four legs! I found a bed."

Boris said, "No. That is not a bed. That is a table. A bed has four legs, but it is soft."

"I found a bed!" Morris yelled. "This has four legs, and it is soft."

Boris yelled, "Put that cat down! Come here. I found a bed. Lie down on the bed, and cover yourself with these blankets."

"No, no," said Boris. "Do not cover ALL of you."

Morris uncovered his hoofs.

Boris asked, "Why did you leave your head covered?"

Morris said, "Because my head has the cold."

Boris said, "Your head should not be covered."

Morris said, "AHH . . . AHH . . . AHH . . . CHOOO!" Morris sneezed. Boris covered Morris' head.

"Here," said Boris. "I found a box of tissues. Pull out the tissue, like this. Blow your nose into the tissue."

Boris growled, "You are pulling out a lot of tissues."

Morris said, "I have a lot of nose."

Morris coughed. Boris asked, "How does your throat feel?"

Morris said, "Hairy."

"No, no," said Boris. "I don't mean outside. How does it feel INSIDE?"

Morris said, "I will see. . . . "

"No! No! No!" Boris shouted. "Ohhh—just open your mouth. Let me look inside."

Boris said, "You have a sore throat. I know what is good for it. I will make you some hot tea."

"Hot what?" asked Morris.

Boris said, "TEA. Don't you know what tea is?"

"Yes," said Morris. "I know what it is. T is a letter, like A, B, C, D . . ."

"No! No!" Boris yelled. "Tea is . . . Oh, wait—I will show you. This is tea," said Boris. "Drink it. It will make your sore throat feel better."

Morris coughed again.

"Here," said Boris. "I found a cough drop."

Morris asked, "A cough what?"

Boris said, "Drop."

"No! No!" Boris shouted. "Put it in your mouth. It will make your sore throat feel better."

Boris growled, "You CHEWED it! You should just suck cough drops."

Morris said, "I am hungry."

"All right," said Boris. "I will make you something to eat. But first, stick out your tongue."

Morris said, "I will not stick out my tongue. That is not nice."

Boris shouted, "Stick out your tongue!" Morris stuck out his tongue. "STOP!" Boris roared. "That is not nice!"

Morris said, "I told you it was not nice."

Boris growled, "That's because you did it the wrong way. Look—this is how to stick out your tongue."

Boris looked at Morris's tongue. "Oh," Boris said, "your stomach is upset."

Morris asked, "Did you see all the way down to my stomach?"

"No," said Boris. "I did not see all the way down to your stomach. I just saw your tongue. Your tongue is white. That means your stomach is upset. I know what you should eat. I will make you some soup."

"Some what?" asked Morris.

"Soup," said Boris. "Soup is . . . Oh, wait—I will show you."

Boris said, "Here is a bowl of nice hot soup." Morris licked the soup.

"No," said Boris. "Use the spoon."
Morris used the spoon. "No, no," said
Boris. "Put the spoon in your mouth."
Morris put the spoon in his mouth.
"No! No! No!" Boris shouted. "Give me
the spoon!" Boris fed Morris the soup.

Boris ate some soup, too. Then
Boris said, "It is getting dark. Go to
sleep. If your cold is better in the
morning I will make you a big breakfast."

"A big what?" Morris asked.

Boris said, "Breakfast. Breakfast
is—Oh! Go to sleep!"

In the morning Morris said, "My nose is not walking. My head is not hot. My cold is better. Make me a big breakfast."

"All right," said Boris the Bear. "But you have to do something for me . . ."

Morris asked, "What?"

"DON'T EVER GET SICK AGAIN!"

CHECK FOR UNDERSTANDING

1. What did Morris think *forehead* and *tea* meant?
2. Why did Morris and Boris have trouble talking to each other?
3. What kind of story is this?

WRITE ABOUT *"Morris Has a Cold"*

Boris took care of Morris. Who takes care of you when you get sick? How do they help you? Write a paragraph about it.

YOU CAN MAKE A PUPPET

Did you ever want to make your own puppet? When you follow these directions and use your imagination, that's exactly what you will do!

Here's what you will need:
    2 paper plates (not the waxy kind)
    paste, glue, or a stapler
    scissors
    crayons or colored pencils
    construction paper
    scraps of fabric, yarn, or other odds
        and ends

This is what you do:

1 Decide what kind of expression your puppet will have. You can make it scary or funny. Your puppet can look like a clown or someone from Mars, or maybe an animal—a bear or a cat. Anything you decide is fine.

69

2 Fold one paper plate in half; press the fold. Open up the plate. Cut it along the fold.

3 Fold the second paper plate in half. Open it up face down.

4 Place one cut half on top of that plate. Lay the straight edge of the cut half against the fold of the plate.

5 Glue or staple the plates together along the outer edges. Do not glue along the straight edge. Your fingers must fit inside this pocket.

6 Color the inside of the plate to make the mouth. Add teeth, fangs, or a tongue. Glue them inside the mouth.

7 Make funny-looking eyes and ears. Make them stand up on top of the head. Add hair, whiskers, a hat, or . . . ?

8 To make dangling legs, fold long strips of paper back and forth. Glue them to the bottom.

9 To make your puppet "talk," put four fingers inside the pocket. Then open and close your hand. Give your puppet a name and then put on a great show!

long **e** spelled **ie**

berry	lady	penny	puppy
berries	ladies	pennies	puppies
field	piece	chief	belief
yield	niece	brief	believe

long **e** spelled **ei**

ceiling	receive	either	neither

Farmer Neil's Field

Farmer Neil's field
    Is a wonderful spot,
The weather is fine,
    Neither cold nor hot.

Playful puppies
    Scamper over the ground,
Bushes have berries
    That are sweet and round.

73

You can shout and shriek,
　　Do just what you please,
Roll in sweet, green grass
　　Or climb apple trees.

The sky above
　　Is a ceiling of blue,
The grass, a soft carpet
　　Underneath you.

Spend just a brief time
　　Or stay the whole day,
You're sure to have fun in the field
　　Either way.

Leo, Zack, and Emmie

by Amy Ehrlich

What if a new classmate became best friends with your best friend? In this story, Zack's feelings are hurt. How does he feel by the end of the story?

Part 1: A New Girl

There was a new girl in Zack and Leo's class. "Class," said Miss Davis, "this is Emmie Williams. Please make her feel welcome in Room 208."

Miss Davis turned to write some numbers on the blackboard. Emmie Williams wiggled her ears. No one saw but Zack. He had tried to wiggle his ears for years.

"Want to come over to my house?"
Leo said to Zack after school. "I have a
brand-new robot." But Zack was
waiting for Emmie.

"Maybe I'll come later," he said.
Emmie came into the schoolyard.
"Hi," said Zack. "I know how to cross
my eyes."

"Big deal," said Emmie. She crossed
her eyes and looked at him. Then she
wiggled her ears. "See you," she said,
and walked away.

Zack went to Leo's house. He went
into the bathroom and closed the door.
Then he looked in the mirror. He held
his ears with his fingers. He moved them
up and down. It was no use. When he
took his fingers away, his ears stayed
right where they were.

"Come on out of the bathroom," yelled Leo. "Don't you want to see my robot?" Leo's new robot could walk and talk. It could even shoot rockets. But Zack did not want to play with it.

"That Emmie Williams thinks she's so great," he said. "But I don't like her at all."

Leo shot a rocket across the room. "I think she's nice," he said. "Did you see how fast she ran at playtime? She knows the names of all the dinosaurs." Zack did not want to hear about it.

79

"I'll show her," he said. "Emmie Williams thinks wiggling her ears is the best thing anyone could ever do."

"Well, that's not so much," said Leo. He put the robot carefully in its box. He took off his baseball cap. Then he wiggled his ears up and down about twenty times.

"Leo!" Zack yelled. "You never told me you could wiggle your ears."

"You never asked me," said Leo. "It's easy. I'll show you how." Zack and Leo practiced until Zack got it right. Then they wiggled their ears at each other for the rest of the afternoon.

Part 2: Show and Tell

Everyone in Room 208 was sitting in a circle. They were having Show and Tell. Leo and Emmie both had plants to show. Emmie had a potato vine and Leo had a cactus.

"Class," said Miss Davis, "these plants look very different. However, many things about them are the same. I would like Emmie and Leo to do a report about plants for Monday."

"I want to work on the report, too," Zack said at lunch.

"But, Zack," said Emmie, "Miss Davis told only Leo and me to do it." Zack picked up his lunch box and moved to another table. The rest of the week he would not talk to them.

"He's feeling bad about our report," said Leo.

"If you ask me, he's acting silly," said Emmie.

On Monday Leo and Emmie were ready. At Show and Tell they showed Room 208 a model of a giant plant. They told how the roots, the leaves, and the flowers helped the plant to grow. Then they sang a song about plants. Everyone joined the singing. Everyone but Zack. He looked like he was going to cry.

After school, Emmie and Leo decided to try to talk to him. Emmie carried the model of the giant plant. Leo took a lunch box in each hand. When they got to Zack's house, they could not find him at first. Then they saw him. He was sitting in a tree. He would not come down, so Leo and Emmie climbed up.

"Don't talk to me," Zack said. "I don't want you to talk to me." They sat there quietly in the tree. A wind came up and blew the leaves off the branches. It began to get dark. At last, Zack started to say what was wrong.

"Leo was my friend before he was your friend," he told Emmie. "Ever since you two began working on your plant report, you're always together. You don't like me anymore."

"Why do you think we're up here then?" asked Emmie.

"Yes, why do you think we came over?" asked Leo.

"Za-ack, where aaare you?" It was Zack's mother calling.

"I'm getting cold," said Leo. "I'm getting tired of this tree," said Zack. "Come on. Let's go."

Zack climbed down, and Leo and Emmie followed. The model of the giant plant was lying in the grass. Zack picked it up. "Hey, this thing's pretty neat. Was it hard to make?" he asked.

"No," said Emmie, "It was easy. We'll show you how."

CHECK FOR UNDERSTANDING
1. What could Emmie do that Zack couldn't do?
2. How did Zack feel after Show and Tell? Why?
3. How did Leo and Emmie prove their friendship to Zack?

WRITE ABOUT *"Leo, Zack, and Emmie"*
Write a paragraph about an experience you had in school when you felt like Zack.

long **a** spelled **ei**

vein   veil   reins   reindeer

long **a** spelled **eigh**

eight   weigh   sleigh   neighbor

eighteen   weight   freight   neighborhood

long **a** spelled **ey**

they   obey   prey   grey

How Many Neighbors in Your Neighborhood?

by Peg Chagnon

Eight?
Eighteen?
Eighty?

How many neighbors doesn't matter—
It can be eighty, eighteen, or eight.
What matters is the friends you have,
'Cause friends make life just great!

87

Weighing and Balancing

by Jane Jonas Srivastava

Long ago, people weighed things by holding them in their hands. They compared how heavy the things felt.

Later, people compared weights by using a balance. A balance is a weighing machine.

Most weighing machines used today
are called scales. A scale has a spring
inside, much like the spring inside a
ballpoint pen.

In some scales, the spring stretches
when you weigh something.

In other scales, the spring squeezes
together.

When we weigh an object, we compare it with a standard weight to tell how heavy it is. A pound is a standard weight in the United States. In France and in many other countries, grams and kilograms are the standard weights.

The pound is compared with a special piece of metal kept in Paris, France. This piece of metal weighs one kilogram. It is kept very carefully so that it will always weigh the same amount.

All over the world any pound weight will balance any other pound weight. An ounce is a smaller standard weight. Sixteen ounces balance one pound (16 oz. = 1 lb.).

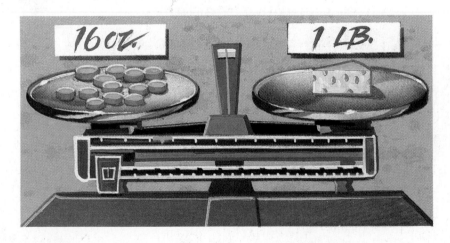

You can find weighing machines in many places. Look in the supermarket. When there are not too many people in the store, ask the clerk if you can weigh something. How much does a grapefruit weigh? An orange?

While you are in the supermarket, read the labels on the cans, jars, and boxes. You will find out how much the things on your shopping list weigh. How heavy is a loaf of bread?

When you are on the highway, you may see a sign on the road like the one in the picture. The sign tells the people who drive trucks they must stop to get their trucks weighed.

There are many other places you can find weighing machines. Look in the post office. Look in the doctor's office. Look in the bathroom.

Do you know how many pounds you weigh?

CHECK FOR UNDERSTANDING

1. Name some places where you can find weighing machines.
2. Does a pound of feathers weigh more or less than a pound of apples?
3. Where is the standard weight kept?

UNIT REVIEW

What Do You Think?

1. Why did Midge yell about balancing watermelons?

2. Why should you stay calm if there is a fire?

3. Why did the Glisson Glop learn to keep promises?

4. Why is it a good idea to know what cumulus clouds look like?

5. Why might it be hard to be friends with Morris the Moose?

6. How is a puppet you make, better than one you can get at a store?

7. Why doesn't Zack like Emmie at first?

8. Why should a pound always be the same weight?

GROWING AND CHANGING 2

ough

muff	tough	rough	enough

The meat was tough.

off	cough	trough

He had a terrible cough.

so	though	although	dough

I'll go, although it is early.

too   through
I saw her through the window.

caught   bought   ought   thought
She thought her answer was right.

cow   bough
Tree boughs bend in the wind.

Did You Know?

by Peg Chagnon

Did you know that you can say
o-u-g-h in six ways?

To learn the six ways in no time,
You should read this little rhyme.

These are words I'll bet you know:
Though, although, and also *dough.*

And these words all sound like puff:
Enough and *rough*—They're not
   so *tough*!

Four more words will now be taught:
Bought and *brought,* and *thought*
   and *ought*.

And now some words we can't leave off:
A horse may *cough* at a water *trough*.

Can you imagine a purple cow
Sitting in a high tree *bough*?

Don't give up, don't be blue—
After this, our poem is *through*!

OLD BLUE

by Sibyl Hancock

Before the railroads reached into the cattle country, the only way to move the cattle to market centers was by driving them over trails. In this story, Old Blue, a big steer, leads over a thousand longhorn steers on an exciting trail drive.

Part 1: Davy's First Trail Drive

"Wake up, Davy!"

Davy opened his eyes. Cookie, the camp cook, was standing over him.

"I'll be right there," Davy said. He pushed his blanket aside and folded it to make a bedroll.

The cowboys sleeping around the campfire would soon wake up hungry for breakfast. And the cowboys riding in from watching the cattle all night would be even hungrier.

A big longhorn steer, with a hide so black it nearly looked blue, lumbered up to Davy and nudged his hand.

"Old Blue," Davy said softly. "Are you hungry, too?"

Old Blue grunted and shook his widespread horns. Davy laughed.

"You think you're better than all those other longhorns. Who ever heard of a big old steer sleeping around the campfire with the cowboys!" He patted Old Blue's shiny forehead.

"You're the smartest old steer I ever saw. Not many ranchers own a steer who can lead all the rest of the cattle on a trail drive."

"Pa said I can ride today!" Davy exclaimed.

"Huh! I suppose you'll feel like a real big shot!" Cookie said.

Davy smiled. He would be riding up front with the cowboys who guided the longhorn cattle over the trail. And if Pa said it was OK for him to ride, then it was. Pa was the trail boss.

"You can learn plenty on the trail," said Cookie. "But right now there's plenty to do here. Let's get to work!" He handed Davy some tin plates to set out.

"Come and get it!" Cookie yelled.

While the cowboys crowded around the chuck wagon, Davy finished his breakfast.

"Let's get moving," Pa said. "You watch what you're doing up at the front with Old Blue."

"Yes, sir," Davy said.

"Feeling a little shaky?" Pa asked.

Davy nodded. "I felt the same way on my first trail drive," Pa said. "You'll be fine."

Davy put on his hat. He climbed onto his horse and followed Old Blue up to the head of the herd.

Part 2: The Storm

Soon the steers were strung into a line a mile long with Old Blue leading. There were over a thousand of them. Davy watched Old Blue walk steadily to the north. No one understood how Old Blue knew directions so well.

"I don't like the looks of the sky," one of the cowboys said. "It could be a norther."

Davy shivered. A norther might bring icy weather, and they had a long way to go.

They had left the Goodnight Ranch in Palo Duro Canyon, Texas, a week ago. It would take two months to bring the herd into Dodge City, Kansas. There the longhorns would be shipped on railroad cars to Chicago.

Davy guided his horse past tumbleweeds rolling slowly in the breeze. Sand crunched under hooves and rose in little gold clouds.

Cattle often tried to stop and eat dry clumps of grass. And when they wandered into low trees, the cowboys had to drive them back to the herd.

Davy looked at the big steer. "Old Blue, you've got your work cut out for you. Here comes the river. We have to get across before the wind changes."

The water was icy, but Old Blue plunged right into it. Cattle and cowboys followed.

The cold water splashed onto
Davy's face. His horse stumbled, and
Davy held on tightly. His horse began to
swim. It seemed like a long time before
they reached the other side of the river.

109

As the cattle came out of the chilly water, they started running to get warm. A thousand longhorns pounded the dusty ground.

"Let them run!" Pa shouted. Old Blue would slow them down soon.

By late afternoon the sky grew dark. A streak of lightning flashed. Thunder boomed. There was another sound, too.

Horns rattled together, and hooves pounded the dirt.

"Stampede!" Pa cried. "Get out of the way, Davy!" he yelled.

Davy rode his horse away from the frightened steers. He watched the cowboys lead Old Blue around in a circle. The cattle followed. Soon most of the herd was running in a big circle. That was called milling. It was the only way to stop a stampede.

As soon as the herd had settled down, Davy rode back to camp.

He put on his slicker and ate some cold biscuits and beans.

Pa rode up to the chuck wagon. "We'll need every man in the saddle tonight," he said. "We can't let those longhorns stampede again."

"Do you want me to ride?" Davy asked.

Pa nodded. "I can use your help," he said.

Davy pulled his hat lower over his eyes and rode out with the other cowboys.

Before midnight the rain turned to sleet. Davy could hear someone singing to keep the cattle calm.

If the longhorns stampeded in this storm, some could get lost and freeze before they were found.

It was the longest night Davy could ever remember. The sleet turned to snow. Davy couldn't even see Old Blue.

Part 3: Belling Old Blue

By daylight, the worst of the storm was over. The cowboys took turns eating breakfast. Davy stood by the fire trying to get warm.

"Hey, look who's here," Davy said. Old Blue came close for a bit of Davy's biscuit. "Old Blue, I almost lost you last night," he said, rubbing the steer between his horns.

Davy said, "When we get to Kansas City, I'm going to buy you a big bell to wear around your neck. Then I'll always know where you are. And so will the cattle."

"Nobody has ever belled a lead steer," Pa said. "But no steer was ever as tame as Old Blue. It's a good idea if it works."

"Davy, you don't have to wait until Kansas City," Cookie told him. "I've got a bell in the chuck wagon that you can use. I'll get it." He came back with a brass bell and a piece of rope.

Davy tied the bell around Old Blue's neck. "There you go, Old Blue. How do you like that?"

Old Blue shook his horns and listened to the bell clang.

"Just look how proud that old steer is," said Pa, laughing.

Davy gave Old Blue a hug. He shook his horns again and rang the bell louder then before. If a longhorn could smile, Old Blue would have.

CHECK FOR UNDERSTANDING

1. Why was Old Blue a special steer?
2. How did the weather affect the cattle?
3. Do you think Davy's dad felt good about Davy's first trail ride? Why?

WRITE ABOUT *"Old Blue"*

Think about the very first time you did something you've always wanted to do, like Davy in this story. How did you feel? Describe your experience.

short **i** spelled **y**

gym	symbol	myth
gymnastics	rhythm	mystery

long **i** spelled **uy**

buy	buying	guy

short **i** spelled **ui**

build	builder	guilt
built	building	guilty

long **i** spelled **ui**

guide	guided	disguise

THE LIBRARY

by Barbara A. Huff

It looks like any building
When you pass it on the street,
Made of stone and glass and marble,
Made of iron and concrete.

But once inside you can ride . . .

117

A camel or a train,
Visit Rome, Siam, or Nome,
Feel a hurricane,
Meet a king, learn to sing,
How to bake a pie,
Go to sea, plant a tree,
Find how airplanes fly,

Train a horse, and of course
Have all the dogs you'd like,
See the moon, a sandy dune,
Or catch a whopping pike.
Everything that books can bring
You'll find inside those walls.
A world is there for you to share
When adventure calls.

You cannot tell its magic
By the way the building looks,
But there's wonderment within it,
The wonderment of books.

Guy the Bookworm

Guy wanted to see the world. How did he
decide to change his life? Did his plan work?

Guy is not your typical everyday worm. Guy is a bookworm who grew up in a public library. His parents lived on a shelf among the encyclopedias. Guy and his family spent all their time wandering through the encyclopedias from A to Z.

One day, Guy decided he wanted to see the world. He wanted some real adventure.

Guy knew that no one was allowed to take encyclopedias from the library. If he stayed in the encyclopedias, he would never get to see the world. He would have to move.

So one bright spring day, Guy began to crawl along the shelves. He moved slowly past the encyclopedias. At last he came to rest in a book on crafts. He was tired.

"Finding adventure is hard work," Guy said to himself. Guy wiggled through the pages until he came to *quilts*. He snuggled down for a snooze.

Guy awakened with a start. The book was moving. *He* was moving! His adventure had begun!

The book stopped at the check-out desk. He heard a person say that his class would enjoy this book. Guy decided that a teacher was checking him out.

Guy spent many days in the teacher's classroom. Children picked up the book and looked through its pages.

He got to know a few of the children pretty well. But he hoped this was not going to be the end of his adventure.

Once a boy named Rudolph Tyler picked up the book and started to shake it. Guy had a terrific headache and an upset stomach from all of that shaking. Guy decided he didn't like Rudolph.

One day, Guy heard the teacher ask Audrey to return the book to the library.

Back to the same old shelves, thought Guy. But he and Audrey were getting on a bus! His luck had changed.

Wow, thought Guy, *this is my first bus ride. This should be a real adventure.*

Audrey saw her friend Cecil on the bus. A few stops later Audrey and Cecil got off, but Audrey forgot to take the book. Guy and the book were left on the seat.

"Wait, you forgot me," shouted Guy in his loudest voice. But Guy's loudest voice was not loud enough, and no one heard him.

Then a lady boarded the bus and started to sit down on the seat.

"Watch out," Guy shouted, "you're going to sit on me!" But the lady saw the book and stopped just in time. She picked up the book and started to look through the pages.

"It's a library book," she said. "Someone must have forgotten it. I'll take it back to the library. myself."

But first the lady had to stop at the market to buy food for dinner. She put the book in the cart and bought what she needed. At the check-out counter she picked up her bags and left.

"Hey, lady," called Guy. "Wait!" But Guy had been forgotten again. Guy thought he would never get to see the rest of the world.

Before long, a teenager came to the market. He saw the book in the empty cart and picked it up. He held a radio in one arm and he put the book under his other arm. Guy moved his small body to the rhythm of the music.

All of a sudden the music stopped. Guy peeked out of the book. He found himself back at the library.

But wait a minute, Guy thought, *this is a different building. This is much larger.*

Guy scrambled across the librarian's desk. He had enjoyed his adventures so far. He must find another book right away—a book someone was sure to check out.

Guy remembered that once a librarian had said many people liked mysteries. He crawled and crawled until he found the mystery books. Guy began to shudder as he read some of the titles—*The Haunted House, Mystery of the Headless Horseman.*

Finally he found a title that didn't seem too scary. He crawled into *The Mixed-Up Mystery Smell.* He hoped he would not have to wait too long before someone checked him out.

Guy soon received his wish. A young girl was checking him out of the library. Guy was excited. He could hardly wait to see where she would take him. Maybe Guy would get to see the world after all. What do you think?

CHECK FOR UNDERSTANDING

1. What did Guy really want to do?
2. Why didn't Guy want to stay in the encyclopedias?
3. What do you think will happen to Guy?

WRITE ABOUT *"Guy the Bookworm"*
Pretend you met Guy in your library. Write a letter to a friend, describing Guy.

ain in **captain**

captain	certain	mountain
curtain	certainly	fountain

ue in **guess**

guess	guest
guessed	guests

129

silent t

fasten	listen	thistle	trestle
often	glisten	whistle	castle

silent n

autumn   column   solemn   hymn

130

WHISTLES

by Dorothy Aldis

I want to learn to whistle,
I've always wanted to.
I fix my mouth to do it but
The whistle won't come through.

I think perhaps it's stuck, and so
I try it once again.
Can people swallow whistles?
Where is my whistle then?

The Turtle Who Wanted to Fly

a play by Carol Korty

Have you ever wished you were someone else? In this play, Turtle almost finds out what it is like. As you read, think about what Turtle learns.

Characters

NARRATOR 1	TURTLE
NARRATOR 2	FARMER
PIGEON 1	FARMER'S SON
PIGEON 2	WIFE

(Turtle may be a boy or a girl)

* from PLAYS FROM AFRICAN FOLKTALES (Scribner's, 1975)

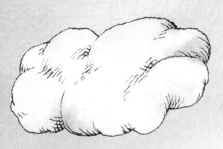

Prop List
(These things can be either real or
make-believe.)
feathers that can be pulled off Pigeons
and stuck onto Turtle
a piece of rope
cornstalks

NARRATOR 1: There was once a turtle
who was a dreamer. He couldn't
run very fast. And he couldn't swim
very far. He couldn't draw very
well. But he could sing just
beautifully.
(TURTLE *enters singing a tune
without words.*)

NARRATOR 2: And because he could sing
very well, he would sing for hours
every day. Sometimes he would sing
about things he liked. (TURTLE *sings
to himself a little song about things
he likes.*)

133

NARRATOR 1: And sometimes he would
sing about things he didn't like.
(TURTLE *sings a little song to
himself about things he hates.*)

NARRATOR 2: But mostly he would sing
about things he wished he could do.

TURTLE: (*while singing, tries to do
these actions*)
I wish I could swim like a wiley green
crocodile.
I wish I could run like a lovely
gazelle.

I wish I could swing from my tail
  like a monkey.
And, if I try hard enough,
And, if I try hard enough,
And, if I try hard enough,
  you never can tell,
  you never can tell,
If I try hard enough,
  perhaps I could do it!

NARRATOR 1: But what he really
  wanted to do more than anything
  else was to fly. (PIGEONS *fly in a*
  circle around the stage. TURTLE
  stops singing and watches them
  in awe.)

TURTLE: Oh, I wish I could fly. I wish I
  could fly more than anything else in
  the world. If I could take up flying,
  I'd even give up singing. Yes, gladly.
  (PIGEONS *fly by again.*)

TURTLE: Birds! Pigeons! Please come
  here. I want to talk to you, but I
  can't go that fast.
  (*Both* PIGEONS *pause.*)

PIGEON 1: Hello there, Turtle.

PIGEON 2: Hello, friend. We thought
we heard you singing as we flew by.

PIGEON 1: It sounded beautiful. It makes
me feel like flying.

PIGEON 2: Would you mind singing
another little tune right now?

TURTLE: Yes, I'll sing a verse or two.
(*He sings his little tune.*)
(PIGEONS *dance-fly until* TURTLE
stops singing.)

PIGEON 1: That was marvelous.

PIGEON 2: When you sing, it makes me
feel like dancing-flying.

TURTLE: Oh, thank you. It makes me
feel like flying, too. In fact, I
always feel like flying. But I can't.
I've tried and tried but I just can't
do it. Would you watch me? Maybe
you can tell me what I'm doing wrong.
(PIGEONS *watch while* TURTLE *tries
to move his flippers and feet; his
shell makes it very hard to do.*)

PIGEON 1: You are trying hard enough . . .

PIGEON 2: . . . But it will never work. If you ask me, it's because you have no feathers.

PIGEON 1: Feathers! Why, at planting time when I lost all my feathers . . .

PIGEON 2: . . . you couldn't fly a bit.

PIGEON 1: Right. I had to wait till they all grew in again.

TURTLE: Feathers! I've never had any feathers. I don't think I'll ever grow any either, because I've been waiting to fly for a long time and not a single feather has grown.

PIGEON 2: Look, I'll give you a few of mine. I don't need every last one.

PIGEON 1: I can spare some, too. I'd like to help you out with this because I certainly do like it when you sing for us. (PIGEONS *pull feathers from their wings and stick them in* TURTLE'S *shell.*)

TURTLE: (*growing more excited as each feather is added*) I'm beautiful! Oh, look how beautiful I am! (*He spins around to show feathers.*) I feel all dressed up with no place to go. Where shall we fly?

PIGEON 1: We were just on our way to the cornfield over there. Come along with us, and we'll have a corn feast to celebrate.

(PIGEONS *fly to the far side of the*
stage, and TURTLE *follows clumsily.*
He is so excited by the feathers that
he really believes his walking is flying.)
TURTLE: This is wonderful! I am flying!
I am just like one of the pigeons.

PIGEON 1: The corn is much better than it was last week.

PIGEON 2: (*speaking to TURTLE*) Are you enjoying it, friend?

TURTLE: Oh . . . yes, it's delicious.

PIGEON 1: (*moving to a new place for more corn, notices something off-stage*) Quick! Fly! I see the farmer coming.

PIGEON 2: (*darting over to look*) His son is with him, too. Get out fast.

PIGEON 1: They caught two crows last
     week. Hurry up.
PIGEON 2: Come on! Fly! Fly! (*The two*
     PIGEONS *exit.*)
TURTLE: I'm coming. Don't wait. I can't
     fly as fast as you can. I'll catch up
     in a minute.
     (TURTLE *tries to fly. He flaps his*
     flippers very hard but, of course,
     goes nowhere. FARMER *and* SON
     enter, see him; FARMER *signals to*
     SON *to grab* TURTLE. *But* SON *is so*
     full of fun and silliness that
     FARMER'S *commands don't get*
     through to him.)

142

FARMER: Get him.

(*They do a funny mix-up here with*
SON *grabbing* FARMER, *who then*
throws him off. Each grabs for a
flipper, but TURTLE *quickly pulls*
flippers into his shell. FARMER
finally seizes TURTLE *by the neck.*)

143

FARMER: I've got him. Go get a rope.
　　(SON *dashes off to get it.*)
FARMER: We can have stewed turtle
　　with our corn tonight. (SON *dashes*
　　back quickly with a rope.)
TURTLE: I'm not a turtle. I'm a bird.
FARMER: You look like a turtle to me.
　　(*They put a rope around his shell.*)
TURTLE: Well, I'm a flying turtle.
SON: Then why didn't you fly?
TURTLE: (*hurt by the truth*) Oh . . .
　　(FARMER *and* SON *start to walk*
　　home, leading the turtle by the
　　rope.)
NARRATOR 2: The turtle was upset
　　but he realized this was no time for
　　just wishing. So he said to himself:
TURTLE: Things being what they are, I
　　think I'd better give up flying and
　　take up singing.
　　(TURTLE *starts to sing, and* FARMER
　　and SON *begin to sway and dance*
　　until they get themselves and
　　TURTLE *all tangled up.* TURTLE *stops*
144　*singing.*)

FARMER: Now, look what you have done!

SON: It wasn't my fault. You were dancing, too.

FARMER: Never mind about that. Get me untangled. (SON *makes it worse.*) No, the other way. (*They get straightened out.*) I'll take the turtle home; you get the corn. (SON *scrambles off.*)

FARMER: Wife, here is a surprise for you. We caught a turtle for supper. Please start to cook him while I go help our son get the corn.

TURTLE: Oh. (*shrinks into shell*)
    (*FARMER and WIFE look surprised.*)
WIFE: Gladly. This is a treat. He'll
    be ready to eat by the time you
    get back.
    (*FARMER leaves and WIFE prepares
    to go to work. WIFE is puzzled as
    she looks TURTLE over.*)
    What a strange-looking creature you
    are, covered with feathers. Shall I
    cook you like a bird or like a turtle?

NARRATOR 1: The turtle felt he'd better
    speak up, so he said:
TURTLE: I think I'm better as a turtle.
    You could pluck off my feathers,
    and I'll look exactly like a turtle again.
WIFE: Thank you for your suggestion.
    It's a good idea. (*She starts to*
    remove his feathers.)
NARRATOR 2: As the feathers were
    removed, the turtle began to feel
    like himself again. This cheered him
    up a lot, and he began to sing softly.

(TURTLE *begins to sing*.) Can you guess what happened this time? (*The* WIFE *begins to dance*.)

NARRATOR 1: When the turtle saw what was happening, he sang all the louder. He sang and sang. The farmer returned and said:

FARMER: (*enters followed by* SON *with corn*) Why, that turtle isn't ready! What is this dancing here? (*He tries to stop his* WIFE, *but he is also overcome by* TURTLE'S *singing and joins in dancing, as does* SON.)

NARRATOR 2: But the turtle kept on singing, and the farmer and his family danced and danced. They never even noticed that the turtle's friend had come to find him.

PIGEON: (*flies on*) Come on quickly. (*motions to* TURTLE) Follow me! (*Still singing,* TURTLE *happily hurries off-stage after* PIGEON.)

NARRATOR 1: And the turtle sang very loudly and walked very quietly until he was out of sight. (FARMER, WIFE, *and* SON *dance off in other direction.*)

CHECK FOR UNDERSTANDING

1. Why did Turtle want to be like the pigeons?
2. What happened to everyone when Turtle sang?
3. What saved Turtle's life?

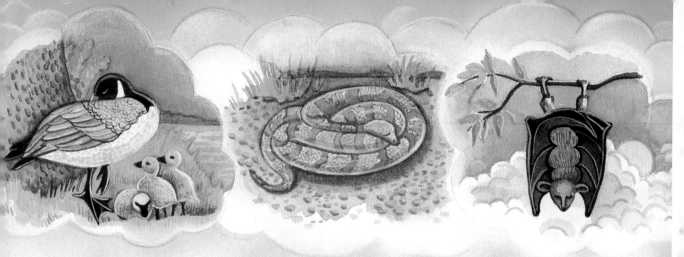

Sleep Is For Everyone

by Paul Showers

A goose can snooze while it's standing up,
A snake when it's coiled in a heap.
A bat will doze while it's upside down,
For all of them have to sleep.
My brother Jonathan sleeps on his face.
Grandfather nods in his chair.
Sooner or later everyone rests,
No matter how or where.

Some people sleep more than others
do. Babies do a lot of sleeping. When
people are little, they are growing and
they need a lot of sleep. When they grow
bigger and older, they need less sleep.

Schoolchildren need to sleep about 10 to 12 hours a night. Most grown-ups need only 7 or 8 hours. But babies, children, and grown-ups—all of them need to have their sleep.

Every part of your body has to rest after it does its work. Your arms need a rest after they carry heavy bundles. When you run fast, your legs work hard. They get tired and you have to rest them.

If people stay awake too long, they don't feel well. Scientists do not know exactly why sleep is good for people, but they know that most people need it to stay healthy.

Your brain works hard. It never stops working. You can sit perfectly still and rest your arms and legs and feet. But your brain isn't resting. It goes right on thinking as long as you are awake. Thinking is some of the hardest work your brain does.

At night your brain needs a rest from thinking. It needs to turn off the world—the same way you turn off the light when you go to bed. Sleep is the time when part of your brain takes a rest.

However, other parts of your brain keep working. When you are asleep, your brain keeps your heart beating and your lungs breathing. Sometimes your brain makes you turn over or move your arms and legs.

While you sleep, your eyes are shut, but they don't see. Your ears are open, but you don't hear many sounds. Your brain doesn't think wide-awake thoughts when you sleep. But it dreams. Dreams are mixed-up thoughts. Some dreams are very nice. Some are funny. Most of the time you forget them when you wake up.

Then you begin to think wide-awake thoughts. You are no longer asleep. Now you feel rested. You and your brain are ready for another day.

CHECK FOR UNDERSTANDING
1. What are some of the things your brain does while you are asleep?
2. Why is sleep important for everyone?

The Muffin Muncher

by Stephen Cosgrove

One day a very unusual dragon caused poor villagers a terrible problem. What did the dragon do? Was the problem solved? Read to find out.

Many, many years ago in the far corner of a very poor country stood the poorest of poor castles.

The only way the people had survived at all was by baking and selling the most delicious muffins in the land.

Every morning, the king, who was also the head baker, would bake a fresh batch of muffins. When he had finished, the villagers would load their carts and set off for other villages in the kingdom.

157

There was never any problem selling the muffins since they were the finest ever baked. But because the villagers were so poor, they had to use all the money they had earned to buy more firewood and flour in order to make more muffins.

So, day in and day out, the head baker, who was also the king, would build up the giant fires in the ovens and bake muffins and muffins and more muffins.

The villagers were just barely surviving. As if things weren't bad enough for them, there appeared at the castle one day a great and monstrous dragon. Now, this was not your everyday, run-of-the-mill dragon dragon. He was a rather enormous, slightly overweight, muffin-munching dragon.

With crumbs still on his face from the muffins he'd eaten at the last castle he'd visited, the dragon came trotting down the hill. He went right up to the drawbridge.

159

Taking one look at the dragon, the
villagers quickly ran over the drawbridge
and hurried into the castle to hide.

The dragon took a great, long sniff.
"Ahh," he mumbled, "I smell muffins!"
This castle, he decided, smelled like a
nice place to stay.

The dragon picked up his suitcase
and moved in, right under the
drawbridge.

He was very tired from his long
journey. So he unpacked his pillow, his
pajamas, and the picture of his pony.
Then he curled up and fell fast asleep.

The next morning the villagers looked out of their castle windows and thought that the dragon was gone. Breathing a sigh of relief, they calmly began preparing for another day.

After loading their wagons with fresh, warm muffins, they set off across the drawbridge, over the soundly-sleeping dragon. With all the rattling from the wagons, the dragon awoke with a start.

He yawned once, stretched twice, and peeked over the edge to see what was going on. "So, that's it! Those muffins look so good, and I am so very hungry!"

He thought and thought and finally came up with a plan.

The dragon jumped onto the bridge and stood right in front of the villagers. He tried to look very ferocious. He roared loudly, "Stop, or I shall burn up your drawbridge!" Then, to be just a little more convincing, he blew a little flame and puffed three smoke rings.

"From now on," he rumbled, "you shall each give me ten of your most delicious muffins as your toll to cross my bridge."

164

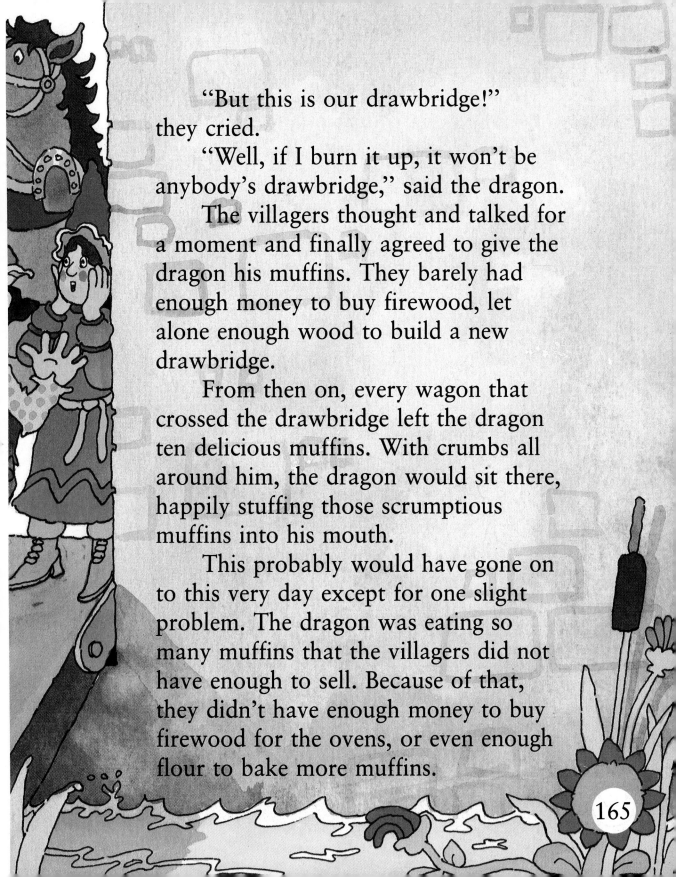

"But this is our drawbridge!" they cried.

"Well, if I burn it up, it won't be anybody's drawbridge," said the dragon.

The villagers thought and talked for a moment and finally agreed to give the dragon his muffins. They barely had enough money to buy firewood, let alone enough wood to build a new drawbridge.

From then on, every wagon that crossed the drawbridge left the dragon ten delicious muffins. With crumbs all around him, the dragon would sit there, happily stuffing those scrumptious muffins into his mouth.

This probably would have gone on to this very day except for one slight problem. The dragon was eating so many muffins that the villagers did not have enough to sell. Because of that, they didn't have enough money to buy firewood for the ovens, or even enough flour to bake more muffins.

They would return every day with fewer and fewer supplies, until one day they all came home with nothing.

With a heavy heart and a tear in his eye, the head baker, who was also the king, sat sadly on a pile of empty flour sacks. He cried, "We have no more supplies to make muffins, and no more wood to light the fires. We cannot bake any more muffins, and the dragon will burn our drawbridge down. What are we ever to do?"

That very same day the dragon woke up, brushed his teeth, combed his hair, and prepared for another day of muffin munching.

He waited and waited and waited. No wagons came, no muffins came, and the dragon's stomach began to rumble, grumble, and growl.

Finally he decided to enter the castle and find out what happened to all his muffins.

The dragon wandered through the castle until he reached the bakery. Then he peeked inside. "Where are my muffins?" he rumbled. "I've been waiting and waiting and waiting! *Where are my muffins?*"

The head baker, who was also the king, walked up to the dragon as bravely as he could. "Mr. Dragon," he said, "we are poor villagers, living in a poor castle which has very little. Before you came, the muffins we sold barely paid for our firewood and supplies. Now that we have to give you so many muffins, we can't afford to buy enough firewood. And our ovens have no heat."

The dragon thought and thought. Finally, a great big smile crossed his face. "I have it!" he shouted. He asked the head baker, who was also the king, to call all the villagers to the castle so that he could tell them of his marvelous plan.

Then and for always, the dragon heated the ovens of the bakery with his mighty flame. With the extra money they saved, the villagers could easily afford to leave a generous stack of muffins for the muffin-munching dragon.

While heating up the ovens
With a lot of style and grace,
The muffin muncher smiles a smile
With crumbs upon his face.

CHECK FOR UNDERSTANDING
1. How did the villagers make a living?
2. How did the dragon cause problems for the villagers?
3. What was the dragon like at the beginning of the story? At the end?

The Terrible Thing That Happened at Our House

by Marge Blaine

Most people don't like changes. But changes can make life better. This is the story of a family that must change. Do things get better for them?

My mother used to be a real mother. In the morning, when my brother and I left for school, she'd kiss us and wave good-by.

"Have a nice day, darling. Be good, honey," she'd say as we went out the door.

When we came home for lunch, we'd have toasted cheese sandwiches or tuna on a bun.

After school she'd listen to us tell about who had a stomachache, or what happened to Abby on the stairs. She'd even listen to me explain what happened when I dropped my box of colored markers all over the floor. Then she'd pour us a glass of milk and give us a snack.

Afterwards, we'd go outside or have friends come and play at our house. My mother always had time to read to us and help us make things and take us to the park.

BUT THEN SOMETHING
TERRIBLE HAPPENED TO CHANGE
ALL THAT.

My mother went back to being a science teacher. She said it was important work. I always thought taking care of us was pretty important. But she said we could do a lot more for ourselves than we did.

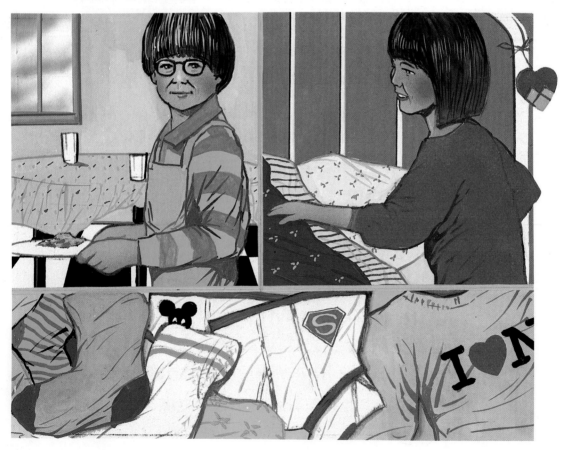

That's when everything began to be different. In the mornings we had to rush around making our own beds and clearing the table. We had to do this because my mother was busy getting ready to leave, too. We even had to find our own underwear and socks.

We had to eat lunch in school because there was no one home at lunchtime anymore.

I HATE EATING LUNCH IN SCHOOL. The lunchroom smells like fish or frankfurters. . . . And all that yelling gives me a headache.

After school, instead of listening to us the way she used to, my mother would say, "I need a few minutes to clear my head, kids—I've had a really tough day." I told her how the teacher kept me in at recess just because I sharpened my pencil three times during math. She said, "You must have been annoying her, dear," instead of being on my side.

My father used to be a real father, too. He'd come home from work and say, "Hi, everybody—what's for dinner?" Then he'd listen to my brother and me talk while he washed up and changed. He told us things about his office or about what happened on the way to work.

When we finished eating dinner, he'd clear the table while my brother and I did our homework or watched TV. And later, maybe he'd have time for a game. My father used to read us stories every night before we went to bed. But that's all different now, too.

My father began coming home with packages from the supermarket. "I'll get dinner tonight," he'd say. And then he'd tell us we were having frozen salmon croquettes or meatballs in mushroom sauce.

I HATE SALMON CROQUETTES AND MEATBALLS IN MUSHROOM SAUCE. They smell like what we have for lunch in school. Yichhhhh!

My brother and I had to clear the table after dinner while my father did the dishes with my mother. Sometimes he did them all by himself while she marked tests or planned tomorrow's lesson in the living room. And half the time he didn't read us stories, because he was too busy helping to fold laundry.

I tried reading to my brother, but he picked boring books and asked dumb questions.

My parents said we were all much happier now.

Then, one night at dinner my brother kept talking and talking. No one was really listening to him or even heard me when I asked for more milk. I got mad. I got so mad I started yelling.

NO ONE CARES ANYMORE IN THIS HOUSE. NO ONE LISTENS. NO ONE HELPS YOU. NO ONE EVEN PASSES THE MILK WHEN YOU NEED IT!

Everyone stopped talking and looked at me. My mother said, "Oh, you poor thing," and came and put her arms around me.

My father said, "What's bothering you, sweetheart?"

And my brother passed me the milk.

I told them how I couldn't stand all this rushing around every morning. And how I hated eating lunch in school. And how no one had time to hear what happened to me during the day. And how I was sick and tired of missing stories and talks and games and everything.

My parents really listened this time and then they said, "Let's see what we can do."

They decided that if we all got up a little bit earlier, and my father left for work a little bit later, we could get out in the morning without so much rushing.

My mother asked Louisa, who lives next door, if we could eat lunch at home with her kids. She said, "Sure," except on Fridays when she goes to get her allergy shots.

And Ellen, our babysitter, began to come for an hour after school. Now my mother has a little time to herself for clearing her head or reading the mail or doing the wash.

Some afternoons we help to dust, or just pick up. Then she feels more like making things with us, or walking to the park.

My brother and I said we could fold the laundry so my father would have time to read us a story. The socks don't always come out right, but we're getting better.

We take turns choosing what to have for supper. Sometimes I go to the supermarket with my father. My mother is teaching my brother and me how to make hamburgers . . . the plain kind.

After we clean up in the kitchen and get our work done, most nights there's still time to play a game or talk together.

Things aren't so terrible at our house anymore. I guess they're a real mother and father after all.

CHECK FOR UNDERSTANDING

1. What did the children think was terrible?
2. What was bothering the girl in this story?
3. How did the family change from the beginning of the story to the end?

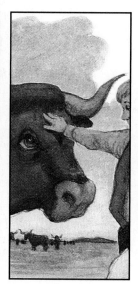

Change the Story

1. What if the stampede had scared Davy very, very much?

2. What if the lady on the bus had not seen Guy the Bookworm?

3. What if Old Blue had not been such a smart steer?

4. What if the farmer's wife hadn't taken off Turtle's feathers?

5. What if you needed only two hours sleep a night?

6. What if the dragon had burned the villagers' drawbridge?

7. What if the dragon had not had such a marvelous plan?

8. What if the girl whose mother went to work hadn't yelled?

BEFORE AND AFTER

THE GOAT IN THE RUG

by Charles L. Blood and Martin Link

"You Can Make a Puppet" told you how to create something. In this story, Glenmae creates something. How does she do it? Read to find out.

My name is Geraldine. I live near a place called Window Rock with my friend, Glenmae. She is a Navajo weaver.

Glenmae is called Glenmae most of the time because it's easier to say than her Indian name: Glee 'Nasbah.

One day, Glenmae decided to weave
me into a rug. I remember it was a warm,
sunny afternoon.

Glenmae had spent most of the
morning sharpening a large pair of
scissors. I had no idea what she was
going to use them for, but it didn't take
me long to find out.

Before I knew what was happening,
I was on the ground and Glenmae was
clipping off my wool in great long
strands. It didn't hurt at all, but I admit
I kicked up my heels some. I'm very
ticklish for a goat.

I might have looked a little naked
and silly afterwards, but my, did I feel
nice and cool.

So I decided to stick around and see
what would happen next.

The first thing Glenmae did was
chop up roots from a yucca plant. The
roots made a soapy, rich lather when she
mixed them with water.

She washed my wool in the suds
until it was clean and white.

After that, a little bit of me (you might say) was hung up in the sun to dry. When my wool was dry, Glenmae took out two large square combs with teeth in them.

By combing my wool between these combs, she removed any bits of twigs or burrs and straightened out the fibers. She told me it helped make a smoother yarn for spinning.

Then Glenmae carefully started to spin my wool into yarn. I was beginning to find out it takes a long while to make a Navajo rug.

Again and again, Glenmae twisted and pulled the wool. Then she spun it around a long, thin stick she called a spindle. As she twisted and pulled and spun, the yarn became finer, stronger, and smoother.

A few days later, Glenmae and I went for a walk. She said we were going to find some special plants she would use to make dye.

I didn't know what "dye" meant,
but it sounded like a picnic to me. I do
love to eat plants. That's what got me
into trouble.

While Glenmae was out looking for
more plants, I ate every one she had
already collected in her bucket. Delicious!

191

The next day, Glenmae made me
stay home while she walked miles to a
store. She said the dye she could buy
wasn't the same as the kind she makes
from plants. But since I'd made such a
pig of myself, it would have to do.

I was really worried that she would
still be angry with me when she got
back. She wasn't, though, and pretty
soon she had three big potfuls of dye
boiling over a fire.

Then I saw what Glenmae had
meant by dyeing. She dipped my white
wool into one pot . . . and it turned
pink! She dipped it in again. It turned a
darker pink! By the time she'd finished
dipping it in and out and hung it up to
dry, it was a beautiful deep red.

After that, she dyed some of my
wool brown, and some of it black. I
couldn't help wondering if those plants
I'd eaten would turn me the same colors.

193

While I was worrying about that,
Glenmae started to make our rug. She
took a ball of yarn and wrapped it
around two poles. I lost count when
she'd reached three hundred wraps. I
guess I was too busy thinking about
what it would be like to be the only red,
white, black, and brown goat at
Window Rock.

It wasn't long before Glenmae had
finished wrapping. Then she hung the

poles with the yarn on a big wooden
frame. It looked like a picture frame
made of logs—she called it a "loom."

After a whole week of getting ready
to weave, Glenmae started. She began
weaving at the bottom of the loom.
Then, one strand of yarn at a time, our
rug started growing toward the top. A
few strands of black. A few of brown.
A few of red.

In and out. Back and forth.

Until in a few days, the pattern of our rug was clear to see.

Our rug grew very slowly. Like all Navajo weavers before her, Glenmae formed her own design. This design would be different from all others.

Then, at last, the weaving was finished! But not until I'd checked it quite thoroughly in front . . . and in back. Then I let Glenmae take our rug off the loom.

There was a lot of me in that rug. I wanted it to be perfect. It was.

Since then, my wool has grown almost long enough for Glenmae and me to make another rug. I hope we do very soon. Because, you see, there aren't too many weavers like Glenmae left among the Navajos.

And there's only one goat like me, Geraldine.

▲▲▲▲

CHECK FOR UNDERSTANDING
1. What did Glenmae decide to do with Geraldine?
2. What got Geraldine into trouble?
3. What did Geraldine mean when she said there was a lot of her in the rug?

WRITE ABOUT *"The Goat in the Rug"*
In this story Glenmae made a beautiful rug. In a paragraph, write directions for making one of your favorite sandwiches.

198

NAVAJO RUGS

These are examples of rugs made by members of a tribe of North American Indians. They lived in New Mexico, Arizona, and Utah.

*G*ymnastics

Would you like to be a gymnast one day?
Read to find out more about the popular sport
of gymnastics.

Did you know that when you climb, hang, swing, tumble, run, jump, or balance that you are doing gymnastics?

This sport has become very popular. Many young people enjoy it.

First the beginner is introduced to the floor exercises. The gymnast in training must use all of the space on a large square mat.

Some of the simple floor exercises the gymnast learns to perform are: the somersault, the cartwheel, the front scale, and the handstand.

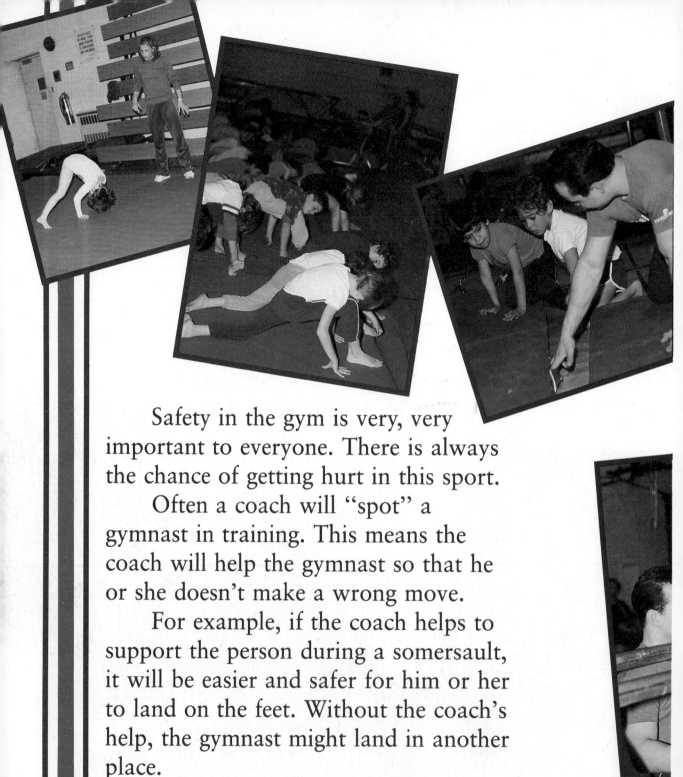

Safety in the gym is very, very important to everyone. There is always the chance of getting hurt in this sport.

Often a coach will "spot" a gymnast in training. This means the coach will help the gymnast so that he or she doesn't make a wrong move.

For example, if the coach helps to support the person during a somersault, it will be easier and safer for him or her to land on the feet. Without the coach's help, the gymnast might land in another place.

It is very important to know the safety rules.

- Warm up before the practice session. Stretch, jump, or jog.
- Make sure all equipment and mats are adjusted correctly.
- Do not work out alone. Be certain there is a teacher or gymnastics coach in the gym with you.
- End each training session with stretching exercises or running.

Today gymnastics is performed all over the world. It takes years of practice and hard work before a gymnast can do most of the movements with success.

You may have seen competition events on TV. There are six events for men: the floor exercise, the pommel horse, the still rings, vaulting, the parallel bars, and the horizontal bar.

There are four events for women: the floor exercise, vaulting, the balance beam, and the uneven parallel bars.

Many schools around the country have gymnastics classes and clubs. You might like to try this sport. You might even enjoy it so much you will want to become a gymnast.

Gymnastics challenges you to perform your very best. And you will have lots of fun along the way.

CHECK FOR UNDERSTANDING

1. Name one important safety rule a gymnast should keep in mind.
2. How does "spotting" help a gymnast in training?

New Patches for Old

by Barbara K. Walker and Ahmet E. Uysal

Sometimes we think we are too busy to help another person. In this story, Hasan asks his family to help him. Read to find out who will help Hasan.

Part 1: Hasan Goes Shopping

One day, Hasan the Shoemaker closed his shop a bit early.

"Tomorrow evening the holidays begin," he said. "I'll buy something new for my family."

For his wife he bought a blouse. For his mother he bought a scarf. And for his married daughter he bought four bright hair ribbons.

Then, looking down at his clothes, he said, "I must buy a new pair of trousers for myself. These old ones are just patches on patches."

He hurried to the tailor's shop. "Have you trousers to fit me?" he asked. "See for yourself," said the tailor. "I have only one pair left."

Hasan held that pair up against his old ones.

"They seem all right around the waist," he said, "but they're three fingers too long. Can you shorten them?"

"Not today," said the tailor. "Ask your wife to shorten them."

"All right," said Hasan. He paid the tailor and hastened home with his parcels.

His wife liked her blouse.

"How fine!" she said. "And what did *you* get?"

"I bought these trousers," Hasan answered, "but they're three fingers too long. Could you shorten them?"

"Not now," she said. "I want to sew sequins on my new blouse. Why not ask your mother? She does everything so well!"

"All right," said Hasan, and along he went to his mother's house.

"Mother," he said, "I've bought you a new scarf for the holidays."

"How fine!" she said. "And what did you buy for yourself?"

"These trousers," he answered, "but they're three fingers too long. Could you shorten them?"

"Son, I have no time for sewing. The holidays begin tomorrow, and I must finish my baking. Why not ask your daughter? She may have some time."

"All right," Hasan said, and along he went to his daughter's house.

"Daughter," he said, "I've bought you some ribbons for the holidays."

"How fine!" said his daughter. "And what did you buy for yourself?"

"These trousers," he answered, "but they're three fingers too long. Could you shorten them?"

"Oh, no, Father!" she said. "I must feed the baby, and then I'll iron my ribbons. Surely my mother or your mother will shorten them."

Hasan thought and thought. Then he hurried to his shop. Carefully he cut a piece three fingers wide from the end of each trouser leg. With his big shoemaker's needle he put new hems in the trousers. Then, folding them over his arm, he went along home and put them on his shelf.

Part 2: The Surprise

The next afternoon, Hasan closed his shop very early. Nodding to this one and smiling at that one, he strolled home. Everyone was feeling the happiness of the holidays.

His wife met him at the door.

"Come in," she said. "Your mother and our daughter are here."

Hasan was surprised. His mother? His daughter? Hasan's mother looked lovely in her new scarf.

213

"As soon as you're ready, Son, we'll
all go to the festival together," she said.
Then she smiled. She had a secret.

"Husband, *do* be quick," said
his wife.

"Put on these new trousers. See?
I am wearing my new blouse."

She was smiling to herself, for she
had a fine secret.

And, "Please, Father, don't be
long," urged his daughter, with her new
ribbons blooming in her hair.

She, too, was smiling about a secret
of her own.

And he went into the bedroom to
put on his new trousers, trousers exactly
right around the waist *and* exactly the
right length. He ought to know, for
hadn't he shortened them himself?

Suddenly, "Eh, vah!" cried Hasan.
"Are you sick?" called his wife.
"No—oh, no. But something has
happened to my trousers!"

And opening the door, he stood
there to show them what he meant.
His fine new trousers hung just below
his knees.

216

Hasan's wife and Hasan's mother and Hasan's daughter all said, "But I shortened them only three fingers!"

Then, realizing what must have happened, they stared at Hasan.

As for Hasan, he stared back at them, too stunned to speak.

Part 3: New Patches

"My dear," said his wife, "last night while you were out visiting your friends, I remembered the trousers. 'He's such a good husband,' I said to myself. 'I'll shorten the trousers while he's gone.' There was *such* a clumsy hem at the bottom of each leg! But I ripped out the hems and cut exactly three fingers off the ends. Then I hemmed them neatly and put them back on your shelf."

Hasan's mother smiled. "I came this morning after your wife had gone to do her marketing. I had finished my baking, and I said to myself, 'Hasan is such a good son. I'll shorten his trousers now.' I found the trousers and let down the hems and cut a piece exactly three fingers' width from the end of each leg. I made neat hems in them and put them on your shelf. I wanted to surprise you!"

"Oh, you did, Mother!" Hasan said, smiling despite himself.

Then it was his daughter's turn.

"Father, I was rocking my baby this morning when I remembered your trousers. 'He's such a kind father,' I said to myself. 'I *must* shorten his trousers.' So I bundled up the baby and hurried over here. I found the trousers on your shelf and took out the hems and trimmed three fingers' width from each leg and put in new hems.

"Then I folded the trousers and put them back on your shelf and took the baby along home. I wanted it to be a nice surprise for you."

Hasan looked from one to the other. Then he laughed.

"But I had already shortened them myself!"

"You?" they exclaimed.

"Yes. Someone had to do it, so I cut off the ends and hemmed them up myself."

Suddenly they all shouted with laughter. And, in the middle of their laughing, they thought what they could do; they could sew all the pieces back onto the trousers. As luck would have it, when they had finished, the trousers were exactly the right length.

"Well, my dears," said Hasan, "at least all my patches are *new* patches!"

And, dressed in their holiday finery, away they went to the festival.

CHECK FOR UNDERSTANDING
1. What was wrong with Hasan's new trousers?
2. How did Hasan's family surprise him?
3. How did the family solve the problem?

Nate the Great and the STICKY CASE

by Marjorie Weinman Sharmat

Nate the Great is a detective. His friend Claude asks Nate to help him find something. Is it big or small? Follow Nate as he solves the mystery.

I, Nate the Great, was drying off
from the rain. I was sitting under a
blanket and reading a detective book.
My dog Sludge was sniffing it. I was on
page 33 when I heard a knock. I opened
the door. Claude was there.

"I lost my best dinosaur," Claude
said.

He was always losing things.

"This is your biggest loss yet," I
said. "A dinosaur is huge. How could
you lose it?"

"My dinosaur is small," Claude said.
"It is a stegosaurus on a stamp.
Can you help me find it?"

"It is hard to find something that
small," I said. "This will be a big case.
But I will take it. Tell me, where was
the stegosaurus stamp the last time you
saw it?"

"It was on a table in my house,"
Claude said. "I was showing all my
dinosaur stamps to my friends. The
stegosaurus stamp was my favorite."

"Who are your friends?" I asked.

"Annie, Pip, Rosamond and you. But you weren't there," Claude added.

"Good thinking," I said. "I, Nate the Great, will go to your house and look at your table."

I wrote a note to my mother.

225

Dear Mother,
I am on a sticky case.
When I find something
big that is small
I will be back.
Love,
Nate the Great

Claude and I went to his house. He did not lose his way. He showed me his table. It had stamps all over it.

"Here are all of my stamps," Claude said. "Except for the stegosaurus stamp."

I, Nate the Great, saw a tyrannosaurus stamp. I saw a brontosaurus stamp. I saw an ichthyosaurus stamp.

"Where was the stegosaurus stamp when it was on the table?" I asked.

"Near the edge," said Claude.

"It must have fallen off," I said.

I looked on the floor near the table. The stegosaurus stamp was not there. I picked up a stamp and showed it to Sludge.

"We must look for a lost stamp,"
I said.

Sometimes Sludge is not a great
detective. He tried to lick the sticky side
of the stamp.

"Look! Don't lick," I said.

Sludge and I looked at, over,
under, and around everything in
Claude's house. We did not find the
stegosaurus stamp.

I, Nate the Great, turned to Claude.
"The stegosaurus stamp is not in your
house," I said. "Tell me, when did you
notice the stamp missing?"

"After everybody left," Claude said.

"Did everybody leave together?"
I asked.

"Yes," said Claude.

"Did everybody come together?"
I asked.

"No," said Claude. "Annie and Rosamond came to tell me that Rosamond was going to have a yard sale. Then it started to rain. It rained for a long time. So Annie and Rosamond stayed and looked at my stamps. When the rain stopped, Pip came over. He looked at my stamps, too. Then they all left together to go to Rosamond's yard sale."

"Then I, Nate the Great, must go to the yard sale, too," I said. "I must speak to everyone who was in the room with the stegosaurus stamp."

Sludge and I went to Rosamond's house. Rosamond was standing in her yard with her four cats under a sign.

"Are you selling your cats?" I asked.

"No," Rosamond said. "I am selling and swapping empty tuna fish cans, slippers, spare cat hairs, toothbrushes, pictures of milk, spoons, and all sorts of things."

"Do you have a stegosaurus stamp?" I asked.

"No," Rosamond said. "But I saw one at Claude's house, near the edge of his table."

"Thank you," I said.

I saw Pip looking at some empty tuna fish cans.

"Did you see a stegosaurus stamp at the edge of Claude's table?" I asked.

Pip doesn't say much. He shook his head up and down.

"Do you know where it is now?" I asked.

Pip shook his head sideways.

"Thank you," I said.

I saw Annie and her dog Fang.

"I am looking for Claude's stegosaurus stamp," I said. "What do you know about it?"

Annie said, "I know the stegosaurus looks like Fang."

Annie turned toward Fang. "Show us your stegosaurus smile," she said.

I said good-by to Annie. Sludge and I walked home. It was a good walk. There were raindrops on the tree leaves. We saw ourselves in puddles. We sniffed the clean air. We saw a rainbow.

At home I made some pancakes. I gave Sludge a bone. We ate and thought.

Where was the stegosaurus stamp? Nobody knew. But the stamp was gone. This was a sticky case. I, Nate the Great, was stuck.

Then I thought, perhaps there is something different about a stegosaurus stamp. Perhaps I should think about the stegosaurus instead of the stamp.

Suddenly I, Nate the Great, felt great. I had pancakes in my stomach and a good idea in my head.

"Wait here, Sludge," I said. "I have to go look for information."

234

I went to the museum. I saw a stegosaurus there. I had to look up. And up. And up. The stegosaurus was big. He was a giant lizard. He lived a long time ago. He had two brains.

I, Nate the Great, wished that I had two brains and that one of them would solve this case.

I walked home. I thought hard. What did I know about the stegosaurus stamp? I knew that Annie and Rosamond went to Claude's house and saw the stamp. Then it rained for a long time. I knew that after the rain stopped, Pip went to Claude's house and saw the stamp, too. I knew it was not in Claude's house now.

How did it get out and where was it?

Seeing the big stegosaurus had not helped the case. Perhaps I had been thinking wrong. Perhaps I had forgotten that there are two sides to every stamp. Perhaps I should think about the sticky side instead of the stegosaurus side.

"Think sticky," I said when I walked inside and saw Sludge. I remembered when Sludge tried to lick the sticky side of a stamp. Sludge's wet tongue would have made the stamp very sticky. A very sticky stamp . . . sticks!

I, Nate the Great, knew that anything wet would make a stamp very sticky. I thought of wet things. I thought of drips and drops. I thought of rain.

When Annie and Rosamond went to Claude's house it was not raining. But when Pip went to Claude's house it had been raining and stopped. Raindrops were on the trees. Puddles were on the sidewalk. Hmmm. I, Nate the Great, thought of puddles. I thought of Pip stepping in them.

I got a stamp from my desk and put it on the floor. I went outside and stepped in a few puddles. Then I went back inside and stepped on the sticky side of the stamp. The stamp stuck to my shoe! The same thing must have happened to the stegosaurus stamp and Pip's shoe at Claude's house.

Sludge had given me the clue I needed. Now I knew that I had to see Pip's shoes. We went to Pip's house. I rang the bell. Pip opened the door. I looked down at his feet. He was wearing slippers.

"Where are your shoes?" I asked.

Pip looked down at his feet. He opened his mouth. Then he said, "My shoes were all wet from the rain. After I left Claude's house I swapped them for a pair of slippers at Rosamond's yard sale. I took the slippers off the Swap Table and put my shoes there."

"Thank you," I said.

Sludge and I went back to Rosamond's yard sale. We went up to the Swap Table.

"The sticky case is almost over," I said. But Pip's shoes were not there.

Rosamond came over.

"I want Pip's shoes," I said. "Where are they?"

"I just sold them to Annie for ten cents," Rosamond said. "It was my big sale of the day."

Sludge and I ran to Annie's house. She was outside with Fang. I saw two shoes. One was on the ground. The other was in Fang's mouth.

"Are these Pip's shoes?" I asked.

"They were," Annie said. "I bought them for Fang to chew."

I, Nate the Great, saw the bottom of the shoe Fang was chewing on. Something small, square, and dirty was stuck to it.

At last I had found the stegosaurus stamp. But I knew that finding was not everything. Getting was important, too. I thought fast.

"Show me Fang's stegosaurus smile," I said.

"Smile Fang," Annie said.

Fang smiled. The shoe fell to the ground. I picked it up. I, Nate the Great, peeled off the stamp. The case was solved.

We took the stegosaurus stamp to Claude's house. The stamp was dirty, sticky, icky, and ugly. But Claude was happy to get it.

Sludge and I walked home. We were careful not to step in any puddles.

You can read more about Nate, the child detective, in a series of other "Nate the Great" books by Marjorie Weinman Sharmat. What case will Nate solve next?

CHECK FOR UNDERSTANDING

1. What was Nate looking for in this case?
2. Who helped Nate solve the case? How?
3. Why was the rain an important clue?

WRITE ABOUT *"Nate the Great"*

How good a detective are you? Think about a time when you lost something at home. Describe the steps you went through to find it.

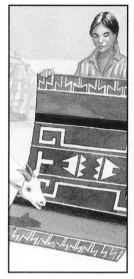   

Why?

1. Glenmae wove a very beautiful Navajo rug.

2. Many schools have gymnastics classes and clubs.

3. Hasan's pants were much too short.

4. When Pip stepped on the stamp, it stuck to his shoe.

5. Glenmae knew just what to do.

6. Gymnastics is fun and healthy for growing children.

7. Hasan's family decided to help him after all.

8. Pip's feet got wet in the rain.

GLOSSARY

A,a

admit, admitted (ad mit) *verb*
The girls *admit* that they came in late.

afford, afforded (af ford) *verb*
Tom saved some money. He can *afford* to buy a new coat.

allergy, allergies (al ler gy) *noun*
Sam sneezes a lot around cats if he doesn't get his *allergy* shots.

annoy, annoyed (an noy) *verb*
Do not *annoy* me while I am reading.

aquarium, aquariums (a quar i um) *noun*
Mike has five fish in his big *aquarium.*

awe (awe) *noun*
Jane gazed in *awe* at the toys in the shop window.

awe, awed *verb*
We were *awed* when we saw the beautiful sunset.

B,b

bakery, bakeries (bak er y) *noun*
Dad bought muffins at the *bakery.*

balance, balances (bal ance) *noun*
Kim lost her *balance* and fell off her bike.

balance, balanced *verb*
The seal can *balance* a ball on its nose.

border, borders (bor der) *noun*
Mom planted a *border* of flowers around the yard.

border, bordered *verb*
A river *bordered* the town on one side.

bother, bothers (both er) *noun*
It is a *bother* to have to wait in line.

bother, bothered *verb*
You look mad. Did I *bother* you?

246

brass (brass) *noun*

The handle of the front door is made of shiny *brass*.

C,c _____

clerk, clerks (clerk) *noun*

The *clerk* in the store helped Jim find a coat.

clump, clumps (clump) *noun*

A *clump* of grass grew by the fence.

clump, clumped *verb*

Jack *clumped* across the floor in his big, heavy boots.

clumsily (clum si ly) *adverb*

Chan walked *clumsily* in his father's shoes.

complain, complained (com plain) *verb*

Polly *complained* that her shoes were too tight.

convince, convincing (con vince) *verb*

Beth gave many good reasons to *convince* me to study for the test. She is *convincing* me to study hard.

craft, crafts (craft) *noun*

Making pots and making baskets are *crafts* I want to learn.

crocodile, crocodiles (croc o dile) *noun*

A *crocodile* has sharp teeth and a long jaw.

crunch, crunches (crunch) *noun*

There was a loud *crunch* when Susan took a bite of the carrot.

crunch, crunched *verb*

The snow *crunched* under my feet.

D,d _____

dangle, dangling (dan gle) *verb*

Ribbons *dangle* from the little girl's hat. A rope is *dangling* from his hand.

design, designs (de sign) *noun*

The *design* in the rug was in red and blue.

design, designed *verb*
I would like to *design* my own house.

despite (de spite) *preposition*
Jill won the race *despite* her sore leg.

E,e

eel, eels (eel) *noun*
An *eel* is a fish that looks like a snake.

encyclopedia, encyclopedias (en cy clo pe di a) *noun*
When Tony wants to get more information on a country, he looks in the *encyclopedia.*

expression, expressions (ex pres sion) *noun*
Ann had a happy *expression* on her face.

F,f

fabric, fabrics (fab ric) *noun*
Lee's dress is made of a fine *fabric.*

ferocious (fe ro cious) *adjective*
A whale looks *ferocious* when it opens its mouth.

festival, festivals (fes ti val) *noun*
Everyone has dressed up for the *festival* to be held in our town.

finery, fineries (fin er y) *noun*
Nina went to the party wearing her best *finery.*

G,g

generous (gen er ous) *adjective*
Mom gave me a *generous* portion of vegetables.

gulp, gulps (gulp) *noun*
The swimmer came up for a *gulp* of air.

gulp, gulped *verb*
The hungry boy *gulped* down his lunch.

H, h

hasten, hastened (has ten) *verb*
We were late, so we *hastened* to catch the bus.

herd, herds (herd) *noun*
Nick saw a *herd* of elephants in Africa.

herd, herded *verb*
The farmer *herded* the cows into the barn.

I,i

imagination, imaginations (i mag i na tion) *noun*
Bart used his *imagination* to draw a picture of a space station.

introduce, introduced (in tro duce) *verb*
Mary will *introduce* Tim to her teacher.

iron, irons (i ron) *noun*
The train is made of *iron* and steel.

iron, ironed *verb*
Sid needs to *iron* his shirt before he wears it.

journey, journeys (jour ney) *noun*
The *journey* across the desert was a long and hard one.

journey, journeyed *verb*
We *journeyed* down the river by boat.

K,k

kilogram, kilograms (kil o gram) *noun*
Kate weighed 30 *kilograms*.

L,l

lantern, lanterns (lan tern) *noun*
Sara lit a *lantern* before she entered the dark cabin.

lather, lathers (lath er) *noun*
The shampoo made a foamy *lather* when Judy washed her hair.

lather, lathered *verb*
Dad *lathered* his face before he shaved.

length, lengths (length) *noun*
Scot's new jeans were just the right *length*.

locate, located (lo cate) *verb*
Leon will *locate* our city on the map.

GLOSSARY

lumber (lum ber) *noun*
We can use the *lumber* to build a treehouse.

lumber, lumbered *verb*
The elephants *lumbered* into the circus tent.

M,m

monstrous (mon strous) *adjective*
A *monstrous* wave crashed onto the shore.

mumble, mumbled (mum ble) *verb*
Ron *mumbled* something. The teacher asked him to speak louder.

munch, munching (munch) *verb*
The horse is *munching* on hay and oats.

N,n

necessary (nec es sar y) *adjective*
It is *necessary* to eat in order to live.

O,o

object, objects (ob ject) *noun*
Carol put a heavy *object* on the papers to hold them down.

object, objected *verb*
Glen *objected* to sitting in the back row.

outrageous (out ra geous) *adjective*
Ray thinks the high prices are *outrageous*.

P,p

pattern, patterns (pat tern) *noun*
The quilt had a pretty *pattern* in it.

pattern, patterned *verb*
Margo *patterned* the dress she made after one she saw in a store window.

peddler, peddlers (ped dler) *noun*
Some people were buying things from the *peddler* on the street.

pity (pit y) *noun*

It is a *pity* that the rain spoiled our picnic.

pity, pitied *verb*

I *pity* the hungry birds in the winter.

plunge, plunges (plunge) *noun*

Let's take a *plunge* in the pool.

plunge, plunged *verb*

Carmen *plunged* her hand into the icy water to grab the boy.

portable (port a ble) *adjective*

Chris took his *portable* radio to the park.

property, properties (prop er ty) *noun*

At school we keep our *property* in our lockers.

public (pub lic) *adjective*

Leroy called his mom from a *public* telephone.

R,r

rancher, ranchers (ranch er) *noun*

A *rancher* needs a lot of land for his cattle.

realize, realized (re al ize) *verb*

When Vic *realized* that he had forgotten his lunch, he ran home.

relief (re lief) *noun*

It was a *relief* when I saw that the vase I dropped didn't break.

S,s

sequin, sequins (se quin) *noun*

The shiny *sequins* on the singer's dress shone like stars.

shorten, shortened (short en) *verb*

Tilly said she would *shorten* my dress for me.

shudder, shudders (shud der) *noun*

A *shudder* went through me when I heard the door creak.

shudder, shuddered *verb*
   The scary stories told around the campfire made me *shudder.*

sleet (sleet) *noun*
   The rain turned to *sleet* and made the roads slippery.

sleet, sleeting *verb*
   It is difficult to drive safely when it is *sleeting.*

smother, smothered (smoth er) *verb*
   Be sure to *smother* your campfire before you leave it.

solve, solved (solve) *verb*
   Chen can *solve* all his math problems.

stampede, stampedes (stam pede) *noun*
   Cowboys work quickly to stop a *stampede.*

stampede, stampeded *verb*
   Cattle will *stampede* if they get scared.

standard, standards (stan dard) *noun*
   Antonio has high *standards* for doing well in school.

standard *adjective*
   Our *standard* snack is milk and crackers.

steadily (stead i ly) *adverb*
   Tracy spoke *steadily* although she was upset.

strand, strands (strand) *noun*
   The rope was made of three *strands* of heavy string.

stun, stunned (stun) *verb*
   Rico was *stunned* when we gave him a surprise party.

style, styles (style) *noun*
   The queen dresses in the latest *style.*

style, styled *verb*
   June *styled* her hair in a new way.

survive, surviving (sur vive) *verb*
   For a while the lost campers were *surviving* on wild berries.

T,t

talented (tal ent ed) *adjective*
Beth is very *talented* in music. She has won several prizes.

tattered (tat tered) *adjective*
Judy's coat is *tattered*. She needs to buy a new one.

tissue, tissues (tis sue) *noun*
Carole used a *tissue* to wipe her nose.

toll, tolls (toll) *noun*
Every driver must pay a *toll* to cross the bridge.

typical (typ i cal) *adjective*
Gary is a *typical* second grade boy.

U,u

urge, urges (urge) *noun*
Robert had an *urge* to sing in the rain.

urge, urged *verb*
Dale *urged* his sick rabbit to eat.

V,v

valuable (val u a ble) *adjective*
Tammy takes good care of her watch. It is *valuable*.

W,w

weave, weaving (weave) *verb*
Kevin wants to *weave* a potholder for his mother.

widespread
(wide spread) *adjective*
The swan took off with *widespread* wings.

width, widths (width) *noun*
The curtains were just the right *width* for the windows.

Y,y

yucca, yuccas (yuc ca) *noun*
The *yucca* grows in the desert and has white blossoms.